W9-DET-656

Silver Burdett Ginn Science
DISCOVERYWORKS

Welcome

to Silver Burdett Ginn *Science DiscoveryWorks* – a science program that engages students in active investigations of scientific concepts. *Science DiscoveryWorks* reflects our belief that the best science education for students is one that gradually introduces them to the knowledge, methods, skills, and attitudes of scientists, while simultaneously recognizing and respecting the educational and developmental needs of all students.

Silver Burdett Ginn
Parsippany, NJ   Needham, MA
Atlanta, GA   Irving, TX   Deerfield, IL   Santa Clara, CA

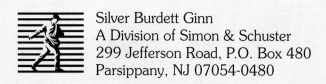

Silver Burdett Ginn
A Division of Simon & Schuster
299 Jefferson Road, P.O. Box 480
Parsippany, NJ 07054-0480

Acknowledgements appear on pages A98, B98, C66, D66, E98, F98, and G66, which constitute extensions of this copyright page.

Grade 5 Unified Teaching Guide   ISBN 0-382-31984-2

Modular Teaching Guides
Unit A: Plants   ISBN 0-382-33476-0
Unit B: The Solar System and Beyond   ISBN 0-382-33477-9
Unit C: Energy, Work, and Machines   ISBN 0-382-33478-7
Unit D: Populations and Ecosystems   ISBN 0-382-33479-5
Unit E: The Solid Earth   ISBN 0-382-33480-9
Unit F: Light and Sound   ISBN 0-382-33481-7
Unit G: Movement and Control   ISBN 0-382-33482-5

3 4 5 6 7 8 9 10 W 05 04 03 02 01 00 99 98 97 96

About the Program

THE AUTHORS
Coming from Diverse Backgrounds, Meeting on Common Ground

Mr. William Badders

Science Resource Teacher, Cleveland Public Schools, Cleveland, OH

A 1992 Presidential Awards Winner, Mr. Badders teaches science to students in grades K through 6. He is a member of the Working Group on Science Assessment Standards, a subcommittee of the National Research Council's National Committee on Science Education Standards and Assessment. He specializes in the biological and physical sciences.

Dr. Victoria Fu

Professor of Child Development, Virginia Polytechnic Institute and State University, Blacksburg, VA

Dr. Fu has over twenty years of experience in teaching child development. She has been involved, on the national level, in developing guidelines for appropriate practices, curriculum, and assessment in early childhood programs. She is currently researching and writing papers on how young children construct knowledge.

Dr. Lowell Bethel

Professor of Science Education, The University of Texas at Austin, Austin, TX

Dr. Bethel recently served as Program Director for Teacher Enhancement at the National Science Foundation. He specializes in the biological and physical sciences, urban and multicultural education, constructivism, and the development of learning and teaching models.

Mr. Donald Peck

Director, The Center for Elementary Science, Fairleigh Dickinson University, Madison, NJ

Mr. Peck's extensive experience in science education includes conducting over 500 hands-on science workshops for elementary school teachers. He specializes in the physical and earth sciences.

Dr. Carolyn Sumners

Director of Astronomy & Physics, Houston Museum of Natural Science, Houston, TX

Dr. Sumners directs the museum's Burke Baker Planetarium, the Challenger Learning Center, and the rooftop Brown Observatory and astronomy lab. Her experience includes extensive involvement in the creation and dissemination of science materials and the design and operation of the nation's first Challenger Learning Center. She has a strong background in physics and astronomy.

Ms. Catherine Valentino

Senior Vice President for Curriculum Development, Voyager Expanded Learning, West Kingston, RI

Ms. Valentino has experience as a classroom teacher, as a curriculum coordinator, and as a director of elementary and secondary education. In her current position, she is specializing in developing materials for after-school programs. She has a background in the biological sciences, particularly in the science of the human body.

CONSULTING AUTHOR

Mr. R. Mike Mullane

Astronaut, retired
Albuquerque, NM

As one of the first mission specialist astronauts, Mr. Mullane logged 356 hours aboard the space shuttles. Now retired from NASA, Mr. Mullane works to bring the experience of spaceflight to "Earthbound" students and adults. He has a strong background in engineering and in the physical sciences.

We believe . . .

As individuals we come from a variety of backgrounds, but, as educators, we meet on common ground. We share a vision of effective science education for all children. Our vision is based on these principles.

Our Principles

- Students learn science concepts most effectively when they explore concrete examples of these concepts. We provide students with many opportunities to construct their own knowledge of science through hands-on activities that are pertinent to the concerns of their daily lives.

- In a world that is growing increasingly dependent on the contributions of science, scientific literacy is an important educational goal for all students. To enable you to help your students achieve this goal, we provide resources that help you respond to the needs of individual students and to the cultural diversity of students.

- Science education is enhanced when based upon reliable educational standards that guide student attainment, curriculum content, and teaching practices. **Science DiscoveryWorks** is based on the *Benchmarks for Science Literacy* prepared by Project 2061, a long-term educational reform project of the American Association for the Advancement of Science, and the *National Science Education Standards* prepared by the National Research Council.

- Students should learn about the big ideas or common themes of science as identified by Project 2061. Four common themes—systems, models, constancy and change, and scale—are used throughout **Science DiscoveryWorks**.

The Authors

CONSULTANTS & REVIEWERS

Teacher Reviewers

Lisa Acy
Louis Agassiz Elementary Sch.
Cleveland, OH

Judith Ball
Coordinator for
Math/Science/Health
School District U46
Elgin, IL

Karen R. Bishop
Ferron Elementary School
Ferron, UT

Jean Blackshear
Fred A. Toomer Elementary Sch.
Atlanta, GA

Bonnie Bohrer
Brookview Elementary School
Brook Park, OH

Robert L. Burtch
1990 Presidential Award Winner
Batavia Middle School
Batavia, IL

Martha Christine
Calypso Elementary School
Bethlehem, PA

Mary Eve Corrigan
The Columbus Academy
Gahanna, OH

John S. Detrick
Emeritus Dept. Chair of
Mathematics and Holder of the
McElroy Chair of Mathematics
The Columbus Academy
Gahanna, OH

Robert C. Dixon
National Center to Improve the
Tools of Educators (NCITE)
University of Oregon, College
of Education
Eugene, OR

Denise Pitts-Downing
James Elverson Middle School
Philadelphia, PA

Michaeline A. Dudas
Science and Math Instructional
Support/Consultant
Northbrook, IL

William Dudrow
The Columbus Academy
Gahanna, OH

Barbara Elliott
1990 Presidential Award Winner
Ray E. Kilmer Elementary School
Colorado Springs, CO

Fred Fabry
Retired teacher of Geology
and Biology
Deerfield High School
Deerfield, IL

Rhea Foster
Anderson Park Elementary Sch.
Atlanta, GA

Linda Froschauer
1993 Presidential Award Winner
Weston Middle School
Weston, CT

Joanne Gallagher
Tamarac Middle School
Melrose, NY

Marlene Gregor
Elem. Science Consultant
Bloomington, IL

William L. Handy, Jr.
Parkland School District
Orefield, PA

Beverly Hanrahan
Franconia Elementary School
Souderton, PA

Renee Harris
Northwestern Lehigh Mid. Sch.
New Tripoli, PA

Rhonda Hicks
James Elverson Middle School
Philadelphia, PA

**Sr. Marie Patrice
Hoare, S.L.**
Loretto Middle School
El Paso, TX

**Lester Y. Ichinose,
Ph.D.**
Evanston, IL

Mace A. Ishida, Ph.D.
Diversity and Ed. Consultant
Blacklick, OH

Kristine D. Jackson
Belleville, IL

Pearline A. James
W. F. Slaton Elementary School
Atlanta, GA

Evette Jones
Grover Cleveland Elementary
Philadelphia, PA

Charlene Kalinski
L. L. Hotchkiss Elementary Sch.
Dallas, TX

**Sr. Sharon Kassing,
S.L.**
St. Pius Catholic School
Kirkwood, MO

John Kibler
InterAmerica Intercultural
Training Institute
Des Plaines, IL

Sharon Lempner
R. G. Jones School
Cleveland, OH

Barbara Leonard
1992 Presidential Award Winner
Heritage Elementary School
Pueblo, CO

Gus Liss
Young Elementary School
Burlington Township, NJ

Jo Ann Liss
Intervale School
Parsippany, NJ

Marlenn Maicki
1990 Presidential Award Winner
Detroit Country Day School
Bloomfield Hills, MI

Lynn Malok
Spring Garden Elementary Sch.
Bethlehem, PA

Barbara Mecker
Rockwood South Middle Sch.
St. Louis, MO

Leonardo Melton
Fred A. Toomer Elementary Sch.
Atlanta, GA

Bonnie Meyer
Tremont Elementary School
Cleveland, OH

Dr. Suzanne Moore
L. L. Hotchkiss Elementary Sch.
Dallas, TX

Kathy Morton
Christ the King School
Atlanta, GA

**Dr. Ngoc-Diep T.
Nguyen**
Director, Bilingual and
Multicultural Program
Schaumburg, IL

Michael O'Shea
R. G. Jones School
Cleveland, OH

Wendy Peterson
Harvey Rice Elementary School
Cleveland, OH

Alexandra Pond
Science Coordinator
North Shore School
Chicago, IL

Erika Silverman
Public School 41
Bronx, NY

Christine Spinner
Parma, OH

Jean Ann Strillacci
Kennedy Elementary School
Succasunna, NJ

Laura Swanson
WATTS Intermediate School
Burlington City, NJ

Arthur F. Tobia
Public School 41
Bronx, NY

Nancy Vibeto
1993 Presidential Award Winner
Jim Hill Middle School
Minot, ND

Sandra Wilson
McKinley Elementary School
Abington, PA

Bonita Wylie
Excelsior Middle School
Shorewood, MN

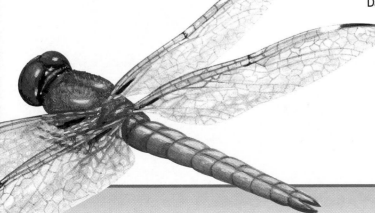

THE SCOPE OF THE PROGRAM
An Overview of Concepts and Themes

	KINDERGARTEN	GRADE 1	GRADE 2
Life Science 	**UNIT A Characteristics of Living Things** Classification of objects as living or nonliving; basic needs and stages of growth of living things **Themes:** *Systems, Constancy and Change*	**UNIT A Kinds of Living Things** The similarities and differences between plants and animals; classifying plants and animals according to one characteristic **Theme:** *Systems*	**UNIT A Interactions of Living Things** The needs of living things; plant and animal adaptations to various habitats; the effect of living things, including people, and natural forces on environments **Themes:** *Constancy and Change, Models* 
Physical Science 	**UNIT B Exploring With the Senses** Using the senses to observe the physical characteristics of objects; grouping objects by their physical characteristics **Theme:** *Systems* **UNIT D Pushes and Pulls** Different ways things move; pushes and pulls; surfaces; directional motion **Themes:** *Systems, Models*	**UNIT C Magnets** The properties of magnets; magnetic force; magnetic fields; temporary magnets; magnets and compasses **Themes:** *Systems, Scale*	**UNIT B Light and Color** Characteristics of light, such as light sources, how light affects vision, and the way light travels; how shadows are formed and changed; the spectrum and color mixing **Theme:** *Systems* **UNIT D Solids, Liquids, and Gases** Properties of solids, liquids, and gases; the changing of materials from one state to another **Theme:** *Constancy and Change*
Earth Science 	**UNIT C Looking at the Sky** Daytime sky and the Sun; differences between the daytime and nighttime sky; the Moon and the stars **Themes:** *Constancy and Change, Scale*	**UNIT B Weather and Seasons** Factors that affect the weather; seasonal weather changes; how people, plants, and animals respond to weather conditions **Theme:** *Constancy and Change* **UNIT D Earth's Land and Water** Properties of soil and rocks; how water and soil mix; how water flows; recycling through composting **Themes:** *Systems, Models*	**UNIT C Earth Through Time** Characteristics of different dinosaurs; how fossil imprints and fossil remains provide clues about Earth's history **Themes:** *Models, Scale, Constancy and Change* 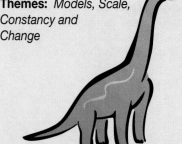
The Human Body 	**UNIT E Body Parts** Identification of internal and external body parts; the functions and importance of individual body parts, including the hands, bones, muscles, heart, stomach, and brain **Themes:** *Systems, Models*	**UNIT E Keeping Fit and Healthy** The importance of good nutrition, exercise, sleep, and proper hygiene; the food pyramid and a healthful diet **Themes:** *Systems, Constancy and Change*	**UNIT E What Makes Me Sick** How germs cause illness; how illnesses spread; prevention of illnesses and injuries; how to stay healthy **Themes:** *Systems, Scale*

> *The science that all students are expected to learn is defined so that students have sufficient time to develop a deep understanding of essential scientific ideas rather than superficial acquaintance with many isolated facts.*
>
> National Science Education Standards

GRADE 3

UNIT A Life Cycles
Stages in the life cycles of animals and plants; changes in animals and plants as they mature; ways that animals and plants survive
Theme: *Models*

UNIT E Roles of Living Things
The needs of living things in relation to their environments; how living things adapt to their environments, change them, and respond to them
Theme: *Constancy and Change*

UNIT C Forms of Energy
The forms of energy and their effect on matter; how heat energy moves, changes matter, and is measured; the benefits and drawbacks of different energy sources
Theme: *Systems*

UNIT B Sun, Moon, and Earth
The physical features of the Sun and Moon; the rotation and revolution of Earth and the Moon; Earth's seasonal changes; eclipses
Theme: *Scale*

UNIT D Earth's Water
Characteristics of Earth's water, including sources of fresh water and the water cycle; water distribution, pollution, and conservation
Theme: *Systems*

UNIT F What's for Lunch?
Nutrients and the types and amounts of food in a healthful diet; sanitary food storage and preparation; care of teeth and gums; digestion
Theme: *Systems*

GRADE 4

Unit C Animals
Basic needs of animals; adaptations that help animals meet their needs; classification of living things; characteristics of different animal groups
Theme: *Systems*

UNIT B Properties of Matter
Physical properties; states; effects of heat loss or gain and of physical and chemical changes
Theme: *Scale*

UNIT D Magnetism and Electricity
Properties of magnets; forms of electrical energy; electric circuits; sources of electric current; how electric current is changed into useful energy
Theme: *Models*

UNIT A Earth's Land Resources
How moving water, wind, and ice shape the land; natural resources and conservation efforts; consequences of producing and disposing of trash
Theme: *Constancy and Change*

UNIT E Weather and Climate
Earth's atmosphere; effects of changes in the air on weather; weather patterns and predictions; seasonal weather changes and climate
Theme: *Constancy and Change*

UNIT F The Body's Delivery Systems
Organs and functions of the respiratory, circulatory, and excretory systems; health measures that prevent or fight disease; harmful effects of nicotine, alcohol, and other drugs
Theme: *Systems*

GRADE 5

UNIT A Plants
Parts of flowering plants; plant cells; plant processes; classifying plants; structural adaptations
Theme: *Systems*

UNIT D Populations and Ecosystems
Dynamic interactions of living and nonliving things in an ecosystem; how energy and matter flow through an ecosystem; biomes; biodiversity
Theme: *Systems*

UNIT C Energy, Work, and Machines
Properties of energy, including its forms, ability to change form, and effects; friction; simple machines
Theme: *Systems*

UNIT F Light and Sound
Properties of light; lenses and their uses; color; properties of sound; the sense of hearing; controlling, recording, and transmitting sound
Theme: *Models*

UNIT B The Solar System and Beyond
The night sky; how astronomers learn about space; the solar system; stars and galaxies; survival in space
Theme: *Scale*

UNIT E The Solid Earth
Properties and uses of minerals and rocks; the rock cycle; Earth's structure; fossils as clues to the age of rocks; the formation of mountains; faults
Theme: *Constancy and Change*

UNIT G Movement and Control
Organs and functions of the skeletal and muscular systems; avoiding bone and muscle injuries; organs and functions of the nervous system; harmful effects of tobacco, alcohol, and other drugs
Theme: *Systems*

GRADE 6

UNIT A Cells and Microbes
Structure and life processes of cells, including mitosis; protists and fungi; bacteria and viruses
Theme: *Models*

UNIT D Continuity of Life
Asexual reproduction; sexual reproduction, including meiosis; inherited and acquired traits; evolution, including evidence for evolution and evolutionary processes
Themes: *Constancy and Change*

UNIT C The Nature of Matter
Physical/chemical properties; elements, compounds, mixtures; physical and chemical changes; acids and bases; atomic structure
Theme: *Scale*

UNIT F Forces and Motion
Characteristics of motion; gravity; measuring changes in motion; friction; action/reaction forces; how forces affect the motion of objects
Theme: *Scale*

UNIT B The Changing Earth
Theory of plate tectonics; the movement of continents; the formation of mountains; earthquakes and volcanoes
Theme: *Models*

UNIT E Oceanography
Contents and properties of ocean water; features and exploration of the ocean floor; currents, waves, and tides; resources from the ocean; ocean pollution
Theme: *Systems*

UNIT G Growing Up Healthy
Human reproduction; the endocrine system and the human life cycle; defenses of the immune system; illness and immune system disorders; reducing health risk factors
Theme: *Systems*

The major concepts for a unit are listed on the first page of that unit in this Teaching Guide.

Silver Burdett Ginn Science
How DiscoveryWorks
in Grades 3-6

The Teaching Guide and Activities and Resources in the Student Edition, together with the supporting Equipment Kits, present strong science content in an exciting and innovative format. Additional materials, including CD-ROM technology, support and expand the concepts in each investigation.

Trade Book Library

Trade Books in each grade-level library provide in-depth science content, biographies of famous scientists, and science-related fiction. Trade Books can be used to introduce each unit and reinforce investigation concepts.

Teaching Guide

The *Teaching Guide* is a road-map for moving through the activities and resources.

Science Notebook

The *Science Notebook* includes space for students to record their observations and conclusions as they work through Activities, Investigate Further Extensions, and Unit Project Links. Used as the basis for a Portfolio, students can use the notebook to generate ideas about concepts and reassess their learning.

Educational Technology

SCIENCE PROCESSOR: An Interactive CD-ROM contains investigations that can be used in place of or as extensions of print materials. Tools such as Grapher and Spreadsheet allow for easy data interpretation. VIDEOTAPES and VIDEODISCS complement specific units.

Assessment

Portfolio and performance based assessment opportunities are embedded throughout the investigations.

Additional Resources

A wide range of resources provides additional opportunities for teaching and learning through different modalities.

Choose from these resources:

Equipment Kits

Color Transparency Packages

Teacher Resource Book
- Home-School Connections
- Activity Support Masters
- Unit Project Support Masters

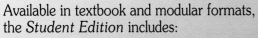

Student Edition

Available in textbook and modular formats, the *Student Edition* includes:

Activities - provide students with opportunities for hands-on explorations

Resources - present science content in several engaging formats

Assessment Guide

This guide offers a wealth of assessment choices including objective tests, performance tests, and strategies for compiling and assessing portfolios.

The guide contains:
- Checklists for Observation and Interview
- Investigation Reviews
- Chapter Tests
- Unit Written and Performance Tests

3-6 Components

Student Editions
- Grade Level Book
- Module Books for each unit

Teaching Guide

Science Notebook

Science Notebook, Teacher Edition

Assessment Guide

Teacher Resource Book
- Home-School Connections
- Activity Support Masters
- Unit Project Support Masters

Color Transparency Package

Trade Books
- Grade Level Libraries
- Individual Copies

Technology Packages
- Science Processor: An Interactive CD-ROM
- Problem-Solving Videodiscs

Professional Handbook

Equipment Kits
- Grade Level Kits
- Module Kits
- Consumable Kits

A Learning Model for

Silver Burdett Ginn Science
DiscoveryWorks

Flexibility is an important feature of the **Science DiscoveryWorks** *program. Although the Teaching Guide suggests ways in which you can use the program compo-nents to organize and guide each lesson, you can adapt these suggestions or develop your own teaching strategies. The model shown here is one way of teaching a unit.*

Get Ready to Investigate!
Using the Unit Opener

Use the **unit opener** to engage students' interest in the topic to be studied. Using the four column headings, have students specu-late about what they might discover as they explore the unit.
- Trade Book: Point out the trade book selections, and suggest that students select one they are interested in exploring.
- Unit Project: Introduce the idea of the unit project. Have stu-dents record their initial impressions about the project topic in their *Science Notebooks*.

Teaching Each Chapter

Setting the Stage:
Using the Chapter Opener

- Do a warm-up activity (suggested in the *Teaching Guide*) that relates to the chapter concept.

- Use the photo and introductory copy to begin a discussion of the chapter topics.

- Have students record their initial thoughts on the chapter topic in their *Science Notebooks*.

- Note the availability of Home-School Connections (found in the *Teacher Resource Book*) and Technology opportunities for use at appropriate times in the chapter.

Investigate

Investigations form the heart of the **Science DiscoveryWorks** program. Investigations are made up of two types of student pages—**Activities and Resources**.

Activate Prior Knowledge

Use the suggested baseline assessment in the *Teaching Guide* to determine what students already know. Then revisit these assessments at the end of each Investigation to allow students to look back at what they've learned.

Provide Hands-on Experiences with Activities

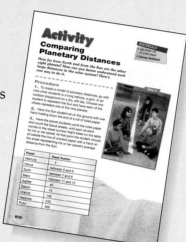

Doing hands-on activities first provides students with concrete experiences that make subsequent readings more meaningful. These experiences will help form the basis of conceptual development.

- Choose one or more Activities for each Investigation. Have students record their observations, data, and responses in their *Science Notebooks*.

- Go beyond the basic Activity using suggestions found in Investigate Further boxes.

- Have students use the *Science Processor CD-ROM* to make spreadsheets and graphs and to record their observations using Painter and Writer tools.

Develop Depth of Understanding with Resources

Resources are content-rich articles that provide students with information that helps them synthesize the inferences they made while carrying out hands-on activities.

- As extensions, use the Science in Literature selections on the student pages, or the Integrating the Curriculum and the Investigate Further suggestions in the *Teaching Guide*.

- Continue developing the unit project by using the Unit Project Links and the associated *Science Notebook* pages.

Close the Investigation

- Bring the Investigation to a close by having students write the answers to the *Think It Write It* questions in their *Science Notebooks*.

- Supplement the Investigation assessment with the Investigation Review found in the *Assessment Guide*.

Reflect and Evaluate

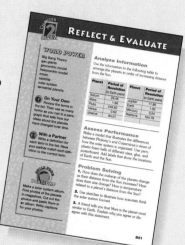

- Use the chapter review found on the **Reflect and Evaluate** page to help students link concepts developed in each investigation. Have students reflect on their understandings by writing in their *Science Notebooks*.

- A formal assessment of chapter concepts is available on the Chapter Test in the *Assessment Guide*.

Investigate Further!
Unit Wrap-up

After completing the chapters, re-emphasize the big idea of the unit using one or more suggestions from **Investigate Further!**

- For students who have completed the unit project, a Big Event for wrapping up the project is suggested.

- Ideas for further research and experiments related to unit topics are also suggested.

- As a final assessment, use the Unit Test and/or the Unit Performance Test found in the *Assessment Guide*.

The Role of SCIENTIFIC THINKING

> *The scientific way of thinking is neither mysterious nor exclusive. The skills involved can be learned by everyone, and once acquired they can serve a lifetime, regardless of one's occupation and personal circumstances.*
>
> *Benchmarks for Science Literacy*

Developing scientific thinking in students is an important part of science education. To learn how to think scientifically, students need frequent opportunities to develop the science process skills, critical thinking skills, and scientific reasoning skills that support scientific inquiry.

In **Science DiscoveryWorks**, students develop process skills as they actively investigate concepts and evaluate the results of their investigations. They develop critical thinking skills and scientific reasoning skills as they respond to thought-provoking questions that conclude every activity and lesson or investigation. In the *Teaching Guide*, questions that promote scientific reasoning skills are identified by this symbol ▣ .

The common themes or big ideas that run through science, as well as many other disciplines, are another important aspect of scientific thinking. Common themes are identified for every unit of **Science DiscoveryWorks**, and the connections between the themes and the concepts within a unit are explained in the *Teaching Guide*.

Science Process Skills

Skill	Description
Observing	Determining the properties of an object or event by using the senses
Classifying	Grouping objects or events according to their properties
Measuring/Using Numbers	Skills include: • describing quantitatively using appropriate units of measurement • estimating • recording quantitative data • space or time relationships
Communicating	Using written and spoken words, graphs, tables, diagrams, and other information presentations, including those that are technology based
Inferring	Drawing a conclusion about a specific event based on observations and data; may include cause-and-effect relationships
Predicting	Anticipating consequences of a new or changed situation using past experiences and observation
Collecting, Recording, and Interpreting Data	Manipulating data, either collected by self or by others, in order to make meaningful information and then finding patterns in that information that lead to making inferences, predictions, and hypotheses
Identifying and Controlling Variables	Identifying the variables in a situation; selecting variables to be manipulated and held constant
Defining Operationally	Defining terms within the context of one's own experiences; stating a definition in terms of "what you do" and "what you observe"
Making Hypotheses	Proposing an explanation based on observations
Experimenting	Investigating, manipulating materials, and testing hypotheses to determine a result
Making and Using Models	Representing the "real world" using a physical or mental model in order to understand the larger process or phenomenon

Critical Thinking Skills

Skill	Description
Analyzing	Studying something to identify constituent elements or relationships among elements
Synthesizing	Using deductive reasoning to pull together key elements
Evaluating	Reviewing and responding critically to materials, procedures, or ideas, and judging them by purposes, standards, or other criteria
Applying	Using ideas, processes, or skills in new situations
Generating Ideas	Expressing thoughts that reveal originality, speculation, imagination, a personal perspective, flexibility in thinking, invention, or creativity
Expressing Ideas	Presenting ideas clearly and in logical order, while using language that is appropriate for the audience and occasion
Solving Problems	Using critical thinking skills to find solutions to a problem

Scientific Reasoning Skills

Scientific Reasoning Skill	Description
Longing to Know and Understand	The desire to probe, find information, and seek explanations
Questioning of Scientific Assumptions	The tendency to hold open for further verification presented assumptions, encounters, and ideas
Search for Data and Its Meaning	The propensity to collect information and to analyze it in context
Demand for Verification	The inclination to repeat and replicate findings and studies
Respect for Logic	The inclination to move from assumptions to testing and data collection to conclusions
Consideration of Premises	The tendency to put into context the reason for a particular point of view
Consideration of Consequences	The tendency to put into perspective the results of a particular point of view
Respect for Historical Contributions	The inclination to understand and learn from earlier ideas, studies, and events.

Common Themes*

Theme	Description
Systems	A system is a collection of things that influence one another and appear to be a unified whole. Examples of systems include body systems, the system created as matter and energy interact, and interactions of living and non-living components of ecosystems.
Scale	Ideas concerning the differences in magnitude of variables, such as size, distance, weight, and temperature, including the idea that the properties of something change at different rates as scale changes. Examples of scale include the study of parts of a system, the effects of changing variables in equations, and comparisons of size and distance within systems.
Constancy and Change	The ways in which anything in nature remains the same or changes, as well as the rate at which change occurs. Examples include predator-prey relationships, the idea of conservation of matter and energy, and the continuous cycling of matter and energy in nature.
Models	A model is a physical, mathematical, or conceptual likeness of a thing or process that helps to explain how it works. Models are used to think about processes that happen too slowly, too quickly, or on too large or small a scale to be directly observed. Examples include models of atoms and computer simulations.

*Adapted from _Benchmarks for Science Literacy_ (Oxford University Press, 1993).

ASSESSMENT TOOLS

> *Concepts are learned best when they are encountered in a variety of contexts and expressed in a variety of ways, for that ensures that there are more opportunities for them to become imbedded in a student's knowledge system.*
>
> *Science for All Americans*

The key to evaluating the success of any science program lies in assessment methods that help you and your students measure progress toward instructional goals.

A varied assessment program can
- help you determine which students need more help and where classroom instruction needs to be expanded.
- help you judge how well students understand, communicate, and apply what they have learned.
- provide students with strategies for monitoring their own progress and ways to demonstrate their talents and abilities.

Science DiscoveryWorks provides the following comprehensive assessment package.

The *Science DiscoveryWorks* Assessment Package

Learner Objectives	Assessments Available in *Science DiscoveryWorks*	Sources in *Science DiscoveryWorks*
Mastery of content	Observation	TG, AG
	Written Reviews and Tests	SE, TG, AG
	Portfolios	SE, TG, AG
Development of process skills and critical thinking skills	Observation	TG, AG
	Performance Assessment	SE, TG, AG
	Portfolios	SE, TG, AG
	Student Self-Assessment	AG
Development of scientific reasoning skills	Observation	TG, AG
Evaluation of individual or group progress	Portfolios	SE, TG, AG
	Student Self-Assessment	AG
	Group Self-Assessment	AG
Effectiveness of instruction	Written Reviews and Tests	SE, TG, AG
	Portfolios	SE, TG, AG
	Performance Assessment	SE, TG, AG

KEY: SE-*Student Edition*; TG-*Teaching Guide*; AG-*Assessment Guide*

PERFORMANCE ASSESSMENT

Purpose: Performance Assessment helps you evaluate the skills and concepts developed through hands-on activities. In the *Assessment Guide*:

- **Performance Assessment** pages present a formal task for each unit that demonstrates students' ability to apply process skills.
- **Administering the Assessment** provides teacher instructions.
- **Performance Assessment Scoring Rubric** provides a way to evaluate student performance in relation to stated goals.

OBSERVATION AND INTERVIEW

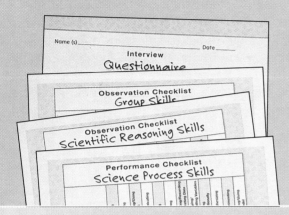

Purpose: Observation and Interview allow you to document the day-to-day development of student understanding using the following checklists in the *Assessment Guide*:

- **Observation Checklist: Group Skills**
- **Interview Questionnaire**
- **Observation Checklist: Scientific Reasoning Skills**
- **Performance Checklist: Science Process Skills**

SELF-ASSESSMENT

Purpose: Self-assessment helps students analyze their own performance. In the *Assessment Guide*:

- **Self-Assessment: Student Checklist** helps students evaluate their own performance by rating themselves on set criteria.
- **Self-Assessment: Group Checklist** helps students analyze their group skills.

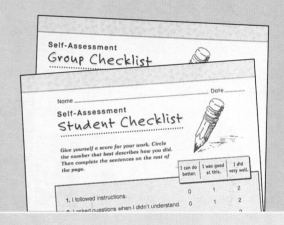

PORTFOLIO ASSESSMENT

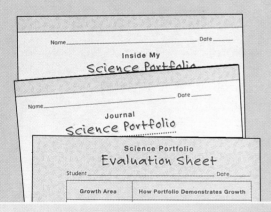

Purpose: Portfolio assessment provides a way of demonstrating a student's growth and progress over time. In the *Assessment Guide*:

- **Inside My Science Portfolio** provides criteria for students to use in selecting work for their portfolios.
- **Journal: Science Portfolio** provides students the opportunity to reflect on and write about their individual portfolio selections.
- **Science Portfolio Evaluation Sheet** provides a method for you to record *how* included materials demonstrate growth.

WRITTEN REVIEWS AND TESTS

Purpose: Written reviews and tests measure students' understanding and retention of concepts at the end of investigations, chapters, and units. In the *Assessment Guide*:

- **Investigation Reviews** focus on material covered in each investigation.
- **Chapter Tests** evaluate students' understanding of chapter concepts and vocabulary.
- **Unit Tests** measure students' understanding and retention of concepts developed over an entire unit.

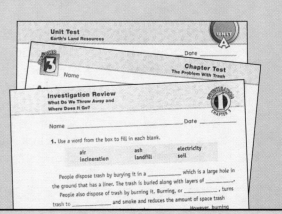

TECHNOLOGY RESOURCES
Extending Our Reach

Science DiscoveryWorks offers a wide variety of technology resources that provide alternative ways of presenting and developing science concepts. These resources also provide students with opportunities to use technological tools and to develop understanding of how technology contributes to advances in science.

The *Teaching Guide* for each unit of *Science DiscoveryWorks* offers strategies for using the technology resources in lessons or investigations. Suggestions include using technology to introduce a concept, as a stimulus for group discussion, as the basis for an activity or project, and to reinforce a concept.

Technology Resources for Grades K–2

Audiotapes and Compact Discs

The audiotapes and CDs feature a variety of delightful songs that relate to many of the lesson concepts. Students reinforce important concepts as they sing along or pantomime the actions in the songs. One audiotape or CD is available for each grade.

Videotapes

Videotapes present unit concepts in fresh and visually appealing ways; they are both entertaining and educational. Titles include: *Arthur's Eyes, What Good Are Rocks?,* and *Keep the Lights Burning, Abbie.* One videotape is available for each unit; grade level libraries are available.

Technology Resources for Grades 3–6

Science Processor, an Interactive CD-ROM

The CD-ROM Interactive software provides an interactive, child-centered learning approach. The CD-ROM provides Investigations that replace or enhance Investigations in the student book, a Science Workshop in which students can explore and create in an open environment, and a customized encyclopedia. On-screen tools include a Spreadsheet, a Grapher, a Writer, a Painter, a Calculator, and a Timer.

Problem-Solving Videodiscs

The videodiscs use exciting full-motion video, animated diagrams, graphics, and still images to create a captivating learning environment for your students. Each grade-level videodisc contains problems keyed to specific units.

Videotapes

Videotapes that enhance or extend science concepts are suggested on the Using the Power of Technology pages that precede each unit. The videotapes are available from many sources; look for the * to determine which can be ordered from Silver Burdett Ginn.

SCIENCE & LITERATURE
Partners in Learning

In **Science DiscoveryWorks**, literature is used to enhance students' understanding of science concepts. **Science DiscoveryWorks** offers collections of grade-level fiction and non-fiction books that engage students in friendly encounters with the science concepts in each unit of study.

The literary elements of the trade books — imaginative stories, interesting facts, delightful characters, appealing illustrations — have the effect of personalizing science concepts for students. They help connect students' everyday lives to science and heighten their sense of wonder about the natural world.

Trade Books for Grades K–2

A total of ten trade books, two per unit, is available for each grade. The *Teaching Guides* contain suggestions for integrating the trade books into *every* lesson. Suggestions include using the trade books to:

- introduce a unit or a lesson concept;

- make a baseline assessment of students' understanding;

- deepen understanding of concepts explored in activities or through the Poster Book;

- stimulate group discussions;

- guide students' independent explorations in the Science Center; and

- prompt student writing about science.

The *Teaching Guide* also lists other trade books for teachers and for children.

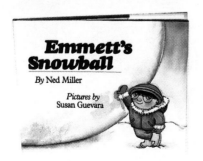

Trade Book Libraries for Grades 3–6

A Trade Book Library, containing a book for each unit, is available for each grade. Highlighted in the Science in Literature features throughout the student editions, the unit trade books provide real-world connections through fictional stories, biographies, and informational genres. The student edition also suggests additional books of interest for each unit that can be used to supplement the Trade Book Library.

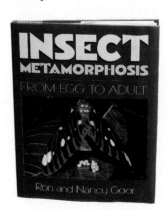

CURRICULUM INTEGRATION
Forming Real Connections

In the **Science DiscoveryWorks** program meaningful connections are made between science and other areas of the curriculum. Science becomes more important to students when they become aware of how fundamental it is to every aspect of their lives. Examples of the types of connections made between science and other areas of the curriculum are shown in the model below.

THE SCIENCES

- Exploring how the areas of Life, Earth, and Physical science are related

LITERATURE

- Using science concepts to explain natural events that occur in a story
- Predicting future events in a story by applying knowledge of science concepts
- Using literature to compare the technology and technological practices of the past and the present

MATH

- Using computational and estimation skills in science activities
- Using different units of measurement and measurement tools
- Collecting scientific data and displaying it in graphs

LANGUAGE ARTS

- Writing and illustrating stories and poems
- Exploring the properties of objects that play an important role in a story
- Building vocabulary through an exploration of science terms and related words

CONNECTING SCIENCE TO

CULTURAL CONNECTIONS

- Exploring the natural environments of distant places and the ways in which people have adapted to them
- Exploring the plants and animals of distant places through the literature of other cultures
- Studying the ways in which people from diverse backgrounds have contributed to science

SOCIAL STUDIES

- Studying the ways in which scientific ideas develop over time
- Exploring the influence of social forces on science
- Exploring how geography and natural resources affect the development of science ideas and practices

TECHNOLOGY & SOCIETY

- Exploring the benefits, risks, and limitations of technology
- Relating science concepts to the use of tools and inventions
- Exploring the relationship between science and technology
- Studying the impact of science on society

THE ARTS

- Using music and dance to express science concepts
- Drawing pictures of natural objects and events

SAFETY
An Essential Element

In order for students to develop respect for safety, they need to understand exactly what is meant by safe and unsafe behavior and what the rationale is behind safety rules. Through your teaching as well as your example, students can develop the "safe science" attitudes and skills that are essential both in school and at home.

General Safety Guidelines

- Post an easy-to-read list of safety rules in a prominent place in the classroom. Review it with students on a regular basis.

- Become familiar with the safety procedures that are necessary for each activity before introducing it to your students.

- Discuss specific safety precautions with students before beginning every hands-on science activity.

- Always act as an exemplary model of safe behavior.

- Have students wear protective aprons, goggles, and gloves whenever these items will prevent injury.

- Keep safety equipment, such as fire blankets and fire extinguishers, readily accessible and know how to use it.

- Prepare students for emergencies by having them practice leaving the classroom quickly and safely.

- Show students how to obtain help in an emergency by using the telephone, an intercom, or other available means of communication.

- Never leave students unattended while they are involved in science activities.

- Provide ample space for science activities that require students to move about and handle materials.

- Keep your classroom and all science materials in proper condition. Check their condition regularly.

- Tell students to report all injuries to you immediately.

For more detailed information on safety, you may wish to order the NSTA publication *Safety in the Elementary Science Classroom* (1993). Write or call the National Science Teachers Association, NSTA Publication Sales, 1840 Wilson Boulevard, Arlington, VA 22201-3000; telephone: (703) 243-7100 or (800) 722-6782.

MATERIALS LIST

Below is a complete list of materials needed for all activities included in the Grade 5 student book. Quantities are indicated for a class of 30 students working in groups of 5. Materials included in the Grade Level Equipment Kit are indicated with a (*).

Consumable Materials

Materials	Quantity	Activity Page Numbers
alum*	500 g	E22
aluminum foil*	1 roll	A42, B58
apples	15	E66
bags, brown paper*	6	A32
bags, plastic (sealable, large)*	75	A76
bags, plastic (sealable, small)*	30	A58, B20, B78, C24, D32
balloons, small*	30	C6
bone specimens	6	G6
bromothymol blue (BTB)*	1 bottle	D33
cardboard (12" × 12", or 8" × 8", or 8 1/2" × 11")*	30	B8
cardboard tubes (paper towel)*	18	B18, F36
cardboard, large piece	6 pieces	F20
carrot tops	6	A58
cellophane: blue, green, red*	1 roll each color	F44, F46
charcoal (activated)*	1-lb bag	D46
clay (4 different colors)*	13 boxes	C14, C46, E72, E80, E82, F36
copper sulfate square	6	A64
corn kernels*	42	A32, A56
cornstarch*	3 tsp.	A32
cups, paper*	88	B76, C46, D8, D32, F61
egg cartons, cardboard	12	E6, E36
fertilizer pellets*	1 bag	A64
film canisters, black plastic (35-mm)*	30	B6
flowers, cut	6	A6
folders, manila	6	F30
food coloring (4 colors)*	6 sets	A8, A22, E74
geranium cutting (or other common houseplant)	6	A58
gloves, plastic disposable*	90 pairs	D6, E22, G6
glue*	6 bottles	B8, E36, E74
index cards*	180	B88, G34
iodine solution*	1 bottle	A30, A32
leaves (broad-leaved, needle-leaved, succulent)	6 of each	A84, E72
leaves (with petioles)	12	A42
lens paper	1 pkg	F30
lettuce	6 leaves	A32
mat, water	6	A64
milk cartons (1 pt)	6	E74
oil, corn*	24 oz	A32, F21
onions	8	A22, A58
owl pellets*	6	D14
paper, blotter*	18 sheets	A8, A48
paper clips*	1 box	C38, C46, F61
paper fasteners*	100	B8, G7
paper, construction (black)*	70 sheets	D28, F76
paper, drawing (at least 32 × 32 cm)*	30 sheets	B55
paper, graph*	60 sheets	D56
paper, tracing*	15 sheets	B6
paper, unlined	36 sheets	C41, D8
paraffin (12 × 12 cm blocks)*	12	B58
peanuts	6	A32
pencils, colored (or markers)	6 sets	A64, B30, B54, B55, B88, C41, D8, D28
pencils, grease*	6	A48
pencils, round*	18	C46, C56
petroleum jelly*	1 jar	A42
plants, bean (with 4 or 5 leaves)	6	D32
plants, broad-leaved, needle-leaved, and cactus	6 each	D46
plants, Elodea (coupon)*	12 cuttings	A40, D33
plants, potted (such as geraniums)	6	A6

plastic wrap*	1 roll	A8
pollinating kit*	6	A64
posterboard	50 sheets	C56, G7, G48
potato	1	A32
radishes	2	A32
salt*	1 box	E10
sand*	8 lbs	D46, E56, E74
sandpaper, coarse*	15 pieces	C26
seed, grass*	6 packets	D46
seeds of Wisconsin Fast Plants™*	72	A64
seeds, lima bean*	78	A48, A56
seeds, pea*	36	A30
seeds, radish*	15 packages	A8, D8
soil*	8 qts	A30, A58, A64, D46
straws, plastic*	12	B78, D33
string*	1 ball	B55, B76, C26, C38, D6, D28, F55
string, heavy (or twine)*	1 ball	C48, F61
tape, electrical*	1 roll	C8
tape, masking	1 roll	C16
tape, plastic	1 roll	A42
tape, transparent*	6 rolls	A76, B6, B18, B78, C41, C46, D28, F36, G7, G48
thread, nylon*	6 spools	E22
toilet paper, 400-sheet rolls	3 rolls	B32
tongue depressors*	10	B20
toothpicks*	1 box	A22, A56, A58, D6, D14
twigs	6	E72
twist ties*	18	A40
vials with lids*	20	E56
wax paper*	1 roll	B18, E66
wicks, large rectangular	6	A64
wicks, small	24	A64
yarn, colored (pieces 10-cm long)*	1 skein	F55

Nonconsumable Materials

Materials	Quantity	Activity Page Numbers
alarms, wind-up (must tick loudly)*	6	F77
aquarium tubing*	50 ft	C16
audiocassettes, blank*	1	F88, F89
balls, rubber (small)*	15	C14, E82
batteries, AA*	12	C8
batteries, size D*	12	F7
BBs (or small marbles)*	6	C16
beakers (250 mL)*	18	D33
blindfolds	6	F82
boards (of different lengths)*	18	C40
boards, smooth*	15	C26, C38, C56
bottles, small-necked plastic (identical)	18	F64
bottles, spray*	1	D46
bowls, shallow	6	E22
boxes, cardboard (small)*	6	F77
boxes, shoe, cardboard w/lid*	6	F77
bulb holders, with bulbs*	15	C8, F7
buttons, small*	12	B30
cans, aluminum (empty)	15	F60
clips, spring	15	G16
compasses, drawing*	15	C56
container, fluted (1 pt)*	18	A58
container, plastic & lid	6	A64
copper wire, insulated *	1 roll	C8, F7
copper wire, uninsulated*	1 roll	E8
cups, plastic*	36	A30, A42, A48, A58, F60
dishes, petri*	6	A8, A30
dowels, wooden (1 cm × 30 cm)*	24	D6
dowels, wooden (small—10 cm long)*	6	F65
droppers*	12	A30, A32, D33
filters, green and red*	6 each color	B54

flashlights (standard, with batteries)*	12	B58, F20, F30, F44,
flashlights (penlight, with batteries)*	6	B58
flower pots, small*	30	A64
forceps, plastic*	6	A22, D14
garden trowels*	6	D6
glass (8-cm square panes)*	6	E8, E38
glasses, translucent, 4 oz*	6	F46
globe	classroom	D56
gloves, gardening*	6 pairs	D46
goggles*	30	as needed
hand lenses*	10	A6, A8, A56, A84, B20, D6, D14, D15, E10, E36, E38, E50, G6
jars with lids, glass (500 mL)*	6	E22, F21
jars, plastic (16 oz)*	12	D46
knives, plastic*	15	A6, A56, E66, E80, E82
lamp with cool-white fluorescent bulb	1	A64
lamps with clear glass bulbs	6	B54
lens, convex*	12	B18, F30
lenses, concave*	6	F30
lenses, convex (A—15 cm focal length)*	6	F36
lenses, convex (B—5 cm focal length)*	6	F36
light bulbs A (TrueValue Krypton Bulb, K-2)*	6	F7
light bulbs B (Ray-O-Vac Krypton Bulb K3-2)*	6	F7
magnets, bar*	6	B20, F88, F89
markers, black*	6	D15, E6, E36, G34, G48
materials, sound-absorbing*	variety	F77
measuring cup*	6	A58
metersticks*	6	C14, C24, D6, F76, F77, G27
microscope slides and coverslips*	1 box	A22, B20
microscopes*	6	A22, B20
mineral sets*	6	E6, E8
mirrors, concave*	6	F20
mirrors, convex*	6	F20
mirrors, plane*	6	F20
model, human skeleton*	1	G7
nails, steel	6	E8
objects, small and heavy*	6	C40, C48
objects, small, of different colors w/1 white, 1 black	assortment	F46
pans, aluminum roasting*	6	B20
pipette	6	A64
pulleys, single*	6	C48
pushpins*	1 box	B6, D28
rock sets*	6	E36, E38, E50, E56
rope*	25 ft	C48
rubber bands, large*	15	C6
rubber bands, medium*	1 box	B58, D32, F44, F54, F65
rubber bands, thick*	6	F65
rubber bands, thin*	1 box	C26, C38, F65
rulers, metric*	15	A6, A32, A64, A84, B18, B30, B55, B58, C26, C38, C40, C41, C46, C56, D8, D26, D46, D56, E22, E80, F21, F30, F36, F54
rulers, wooden	6	C48
scissors	6	A40, A42, A48, B6, B8, B18, B58, B76, C41, C56, D26, D28, E22, F36, G7, G48
screwdrivers*	6	C56
screws*	35	C41, C56
seashells*	10	E56, E72
sound makers (bells*, whistles, rattles, clickers*)	variety	F82
spectroscopes*	6	B54
spoons, plastic*	24	E22, E74
spring scales*	6	C24, C40, C48
springs toys*	6	F14, F55
stakes, wooden*	24	D6
sticks, wooden (thin)*	12	E74, E88
tape measures, metric*	6	B58, G14
tape recorders	1	F89
test tubes, large*	12	A40, D33
thumbtacks*	60	C26
tiles, ceramic (white and unglazed)	6	E6
timers*	6	A32, A40, D33, G16, G34
trays, plastic*	6	D6
truck, toy*	6	C40
washers, metal*	10	B76
wood, blocks of*	30	C26

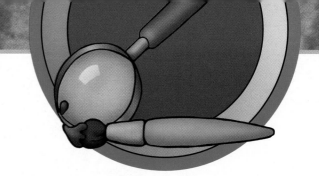

UNIT G
Movement and Control

Overview Movement and Control examines three body systems—the skeletal system, the muscular system, and the nervous system—and how they all work together to move and control the body. Through activities and resources, students discover the components of each of the three systems and explore how the systems function. Finally, students learn how the use of tobacco, alcohol, and other drugs can harm the body by disrupting these systems of movement and control.

Theme This unit, Movement and Control, gives a detailed study of several of the body's most important systems—the skeletal system, the muscular system, and the nervous system. Each of these systems is defined by particular types of cells, tissues, and organs, all of which function together for a common purpose. The three systems are also interdependent; they interact to control and move the body.

THE BIG IDEA

The skeletal, muscular, and nervous systems are the primary body systems involved in movement and coordination. The functions of these systems can be adversely affected by drugs.

Tracing Major Concepts

The skeletal system and the muscular system each have their own functions and also work together to allow body movement.

Subconcepts

• The skeletal system, which supports and protects other body parts, is made up of many bones, together with the tissues that protect them; bones meet at movable and immovable joints.

• Muscles contract and pull on bones, causing them to bend at joints and achieve movement; many injuries to bones and muscles can be avoided by taking precautions.

The nervous system—including the brain, spinal cord, nerves, and sense organs—takes in information from the environment, stores memories, controls actions, and directs the body's responses.

Subconcepts

• The brain is the control center of the nervous system; neurons carry messages between the brain, and all other parts of the body.

• The sense receptors collect information from the environment for the brain to interpret and respond to; reflexes allow the nervous system to respond to danger automatically.

The use of tobacco, alcohol, and other drugs can cause harmful effects to the systems of the body.

Subconcepts

• The misuse of drugs, substances that affect the function of cells and tissues, can cause harmful changes in the body that can endanger a person's safety and long-term health.

• Alcohol has harmful short- and long-term effects on the body and is responsible for many accidents and deaths.

CONTENTS

Movement and Control G1

Standards & Benchmarks
CORRELATIONS

The National Science Education Standards and Project 2061 Benchmarks* are the framework around which *Silver Burdett Ginn Science DiscoveryWorks* is built.

- All organisms are composed of cells—the fundamental unit of life. Most organisms are single cells; other organisms, including humans, are multicellular. (p. 156) *Ch. 2, Inv. 2*

- Specialized cells perform specialized functions in multicellular organisms. Groups of specialized cells cooperate to form a tissue, such as a muscle. Different tissues are in turn grouped together to form larger functional units, called organs. Each type of cell, tissue, and organ has a distinct structure and set of functions that serve the organism as a whole. (p. 156) *Ch. 1 and 2*

- The human organism has systems for digestion, respiration, reproduction, circulation, excretion, movement, control, and coordination, and for protection from disease. These systems interact with one another. (p. 156) *Ch. 1 and 2*

- Regulation of an organism's internal environment involves sensing the internal environment and changing physiological activities to keep conditions within the range required to survive. (p. 157) *Ch. 2, Inv. 1*

- Behavior is one kind of response an organism can make to an internal or environmental stimulus. A behavioral response requires coordination and communication at many levels, including cells, organ systems, and whole organisms. Behavioral response is a set of actions determined in part by heredity and in part from experience. (p. 157) *Ch. 2*

- Regular exercise is important to the maintenance and improvement of health. The benefits of physical fitness include maintaining healthy weight, having energy and strength for routine activities, good muscle tone, bone strength, strong heart/lung systems, and improved mental health. Personal exercise, especially developing cardio-vascular endurance, is the foundation of physical fitness. (p. 168) *Ch. 1, Inv. 2*

- The potential for accidents and the existence of hazards imposes the need for injury prevention. Safe living involves the development and use of safety precautions and the recognition of risk in personal decisions. Injury prevention has personal and social dimensions. (p. 168) *Ch. 1, Inv. 2; Ch. 3*

- The use of tobacco increases the risk of illness. Students should understand the influence of short term social and psychological factors that lead to tobacco use, and the possible long-term detrimental effects of smoking and chewing tobacco. (p. 168) *Ch. 3, Inv. 1*

- Alcohol and other drugs are often abused substances. Such drugs change how the body functions and can lead to addiction. (p. 168) *Ch. 3*

- Scientists do not pay much attention to claims about how something they know about works unless the claims are backed up with evidence that can be confirmed with a logical argument. (p. 11) *Ch. 3, Inv. 1 and 2*

- There is a usual sequence of physical and mental development among human beings, although individuals differ in exactly when they learn things. (p. 132) *Ch. 2, Inv. 2*

- The brain gets signals from all parts of the body telling what is going on there. The brain also sends signals to parts of the body to influence what they do. (p. 136) *Ch. 2*

- Human beings can use the memory of their past experiences to make judgments about new situations. (p. 140) *Ch. 2, Inv. 2*

- Many skills can be practiced until they become automatic. If the right skills are practiced, performance may improve. (p. 140) *Ch. 2, Inv. 1*

- Learning means using what one already knows to make sense out of new experiences or information, not just storing the new information in one's head. (p. 141) *Ch. 2, Inv. 2*

- Tobacco, alcohol, other drugs, and certain poisons in the environment (pesticides, lead) can harm human beings and other living things. (p. 144) *Ch. 3*

*Standards are based on *National Science Education Standards* (© 1996) published by the National Research Council. Benchmarks are based on *Benchmarks for Science Literacy* (© 1993) published by the American Association for the Advancement of Science.

Curriculum INTEGRATION

Science as a discipline does not exist in isolation. An integrated approached to the teaching of science will help students understand how science connects to other school subjects as well as to technology, to diverse cultures, and to literature. The location in the unit of activities that connect to other disciplines is indicated in the chart.

THE SCIENCES

- Physical Science, page G10
- Physical Science, page G18
- Earth Science, page G31
- Physical Science, page G37
- Physical Science, page G60

LITERATURE

- Science in Literature features, pages G21, G32, G60

MATH

- Graphing, page G20
- Making Graphs, page G28
- Statistics, page G50

LANGUAGE ARTS

- Expressions, page G8
- Writing Plans, page G17
- Reflex Stories, page G42
- Write a Story, page G58

CONNECTING SCIENCE TO

CULTURAL CONNECTIONS

- Discussing, page G11
- Surgery Report, page G19
- Write Reports, page G29
- Testing Taste, page G38
- Rites of Age, page G40
- Discuss Ideas, page G59

SOCIAL STUDIES

- Using Senses, page G39
- Interviewing, page G52
- Get MADD, page G61

TECHNOLOGY & SOCIETY

- Knee Injuries, page G21
- Future Firsts, page G43
- Drug Testing, page G54

THE ARTS

- Brain Models, page G30

Neurons and Their Mysteries

by Dr. Dominic Valentino

Dr. Valentino is a professor of neurobehavioral studies at the Department of Psychology at the University of Rhode Island. He was elected Outstanding College Professor in 1993.

CELL SHAPE AND FUNCTION

Our nervous system contains over 100 billion neurons. Each one is specialized to receive information and to send signals throughout the body. Some neurons receive information from the environment, and some send signals to muscles or glands. But the vast majority of neurons communicate with other neurons.

Of all of our cells, neurons are the most oddly shaped. Each neuron has a cell body like any other cell. Unlike other cells, however, the neuron has spidery filaments, called dendrites, which branch out from the cell body to gather input. The neuron also has a cable-like extension called an axon; it leads away from the cell body to carry messages to other neurons.

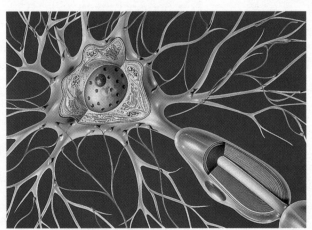

▲ A neuron with axon (cutaway)

As an example of what neurons do, consider the process of discovering a pebble in your shoe. Dendrites from the neurons in the skin of your toe detect the pebble. They send a message, an electrical impulse, from the dendrite to the cell body and along the axon of each stimulated neuron. The axons from the neurons in your toes run through your foot, up your leg, and up your spinal cord to the medulla, in the lower part of your brain.

Axons communicate with neurons in the medulla across a narrow gap called a synapse. The nerve signal stimulates the axon to release chemicals, called neurotransmitters, into the synapse. Neurotransmitters travel across the synapse, where they hook into a special site on the dendrite of another neuron, generating an electrical signal. In this way, neurons of the medulla are activated to send signals to other neurons in the cerebrum.

The neurons of the cerebrum are interconnected in complex and mysterious ways. Neuroscientists believe that our memories, feelings, and motor skills exist in the brain as series of interconnected nerve pathways that communicate with one another in overlapping circuits. The communication that began with a pebble in your shoe may activate neuron circuits that represent the concept of pebbles, feelings of discomfort, memories of a stony path where you recently walked, and plans for ways to remove the pebble.

THE CHEMISTRY OF THE MIND

Neuroscientists estimate that neurons release more than 150 different chemicals as neurotransmitters. Any given neuron uses only one or two different neurotransmitters at its axon endings, but the same neuron may recognize and respond to a number of different neurotransmitters at its dendrites. Neuroscientists say that there is a chemistry, as well as an anatomy, of neural circuits; in other words, a chemistry of the mind.

TIPS FROM Teachers

Give students cutouts of various bones of the human body and have them connect them. Next, have students explain how and why they put them together as they did. As an extra challenge, have them label the bones and describe how they function together.

Anne Faulks
Memphis,
Tennessee

Obtain from a butcher an animal heart, such as a beef heart. Rinse the heart thoroughly, then soak it in water mixed with white vinegar for at least 12 hours. Rinse the heart and keep it refrigerated. After letting students handle the heart, make a lateral incision all the way through it to show the internal chambers and valves. Students love this activity!

Louis D.
Corsaro
West Milford,
New Jersey

In my class, I place my students in many different cooperative groups throughout the year. Early in the school year, I have each student identify some of their personal preferences. Each of them writes on an index card information such as the following: name, telephone number, and birthday as well as favorite color, activity or hobby, sport, food, number, area of science, and so on. Every time I teach a new unit, I use this information to group the students so cooperative groups can vary. At the end of each unit, students are challenged to identify what characteristics or preferences the group members had in common.

Patricia Ramey
Williamsburg,
Kentucky

Skills for LIFELONG LEARNING

Experiences provided by *Silver Burdett Ginn Science DiscoveryWorks* are aimed at developing a wide range of science processes and skills. These tools provide a basis for a lifetime of participation in society as a whole. As described in *Science for All Americans* by F. James Rutherford and Andrew Ahlgren (Oxford University Press, 1990), the skills developed through scientific inquiry foster reasoning abilities that relate directly to a person's outlook on knowledge and learning and ways of thinking and acting.

Process Skills provide a framework in which ideas can be conceptualized, tested, and evaluated. The processes listed here are developed through a wide range of hands-on experiences.

Process Skills

Activities	Page	Observing	Classifying	Measuring/ Using Numbers	Communicating	Inferring	Predicting	Collecting, Recording, and Interpreting Data	Identifying and Controlling Variables	Defining Operationally	Making Hypotheses	Experimenting	Making and Using Models
A Closer Look at Bones	G6	•	•		•	•							
Where Bones Meet	G7	•	•		•	•	•						•
Push or Pull?	G14	•		•	•	•		•		•	•		•
Tired Muscles	G16	•		•		•	•	•	•			•	
Walk Straight and Tall	G26	•			•	•	•						
Measuring Reaction Time	G27	•		•	•		•		•				
Test Your Mind	G34			•	•	•	•	•	•			•	
Reflex Action	G36	•			•	•	•		•				
Ad Power	G48		•		•			•					
Alcohol Advertising: Pro and Con	G56				•		•						

Critical Thinking Skills are embedded in the questioning strategies throughout the program. The chart below summarizes the processes assessed in the Think It/Write It sections that end each investigation.

Critical Thinking Skills

Process	Description	G13	G22	G33	G44	G55	G62
Analyzing	Studying something to identify constituent elements or relationships among elements	•		•	•	•	•
Synthesizing	Using deductive reasoning to pull together key elements		•		•		•
Evaluating	Reviewing and responding critically to materials, procedures, or ideas and judging them by purposes, standards, or other criteria				•		
Applying	Using ideas, processes, or skills in new situations	•		•	•	•	•
Generating Ideas	Expressing thoughts that reveal originality, speculation, imagination, a personal perspective, flexibility in thinking, invention, or creativity		•			•	
Expressing Ideas	Presenting ideas clearly and in logical order, while using language that is appropriate for the audience and occasion		•			•	
Solving Problems	Using critical thinking processes to find solutions to a problem		•				

Through the development and reinforcement of science process skills and critical thinking skills, the following **Scientific Reasoning Skills** are developed. This symbol 🔲 identifies questions within the teaching material that highlight Scientific Reasoning Skills.

Scientific Reasoning Skills

Reasoning Skill	Description
Longing to Know and Understand	The desire to probe, find information, and seek explanations
Questioning of Scientific Assumptions	The tendency to hold open for further verification of presented assumptions, encounters, and ideas
Search for Data and Its Meaning	The propensity to collect information and to analyze it in context
Demand for Verification	The inclination to repeat and replicate findings and studies
Respect for Logic	The inclination to move from assumptions to testing and data collection to conclusions
Consideration of Premises	The tendency to put into context the reason for a particular point of view
Consideration of Consequences	The tendency to put into perspective the results of a particular point of view
Respect for Historical Contributions	The inclination to understand and learn from the contributions of earlier ideas, studies, events, and so on

UNIT ASSESSMENT

Ongoing Assessment

Daily observations and a variety of ongoing assessment activities can provide comprehensive appraisal of student growth. *Silver Burdett Ginn Science DiscoveryWorks* provides several methods to help you monitor student growth.

Performance Assessment

Observation checklists provide concrete descriptions of student behaviors. Performance assessments allow students to demonstrate their ability to use the tools of science and science processes in hands-on activities, at the end of each investigation and chapter, and in a culminating unit performance task.

Portfolio Assessment

Portfolios of student work can be used to holistically assess student understanding and progress. The *Assessment Guide* provides support materials for developing portfolios and in using them to evaluate growth in science.

Written Reviews and Tests

Think It/Write It sections at the end of each investigation foster critical thinking and provide a snapshot of student understanding. Written tests provide additional tools for assessing how well students understand, integrate, and apply key concepts. Opportunities for periodic review are included in Analyze and Conclude at the end of each activity, in Reflect and Evaluate at the end of each chapter, and in Chapter Tests and Unit Tests in the *Assessment Guide*.

Unit Performance Assessment

UNIT G — Performance Assessment — Movement and Control

Name _____ Date _____

READY, SET, CONCENTRATE!

You and your partner will create a card game using drawings of the parts of the human body that you studied in this unit. As you play the game, you will measure your partner's "learning curve" by timing how long it takes your partner to make the correct matches.

Materials
✔ index cards
✔ markers
✔ timer

Procedure
1. With your partner, list ten parts of the body discussed in this unit—five parts from the nervous system (The Brain) and five parts from the skeletal and muscular systems (The Frame). Include a description of each part and how it works. Write your list in the Data Space and, if necessary, on a separate sheet of paper.

Data Space

Students should have a list of ten body parts and a description of each body part. Examples from the skeletal and muscular systems include skeletal, smooth, or cardiac muscles; ball-and-socket, hinge, pivot, or sliding joints. Examples from the nervous system include parts of the brain, the sense organs, and the spinal cord.

Performance Assessment — Movement and Control — UNIT G

Date _____

2. Choose a task. One partner should *Be the Brain*. The other should *Build the Frame*. Then each player takes a stack of ten blank cards, two cards for each body part listed for their task in the Data Space. On the first card of each pair, write the name of the body part and make a drawing of the part. On the second card, describe the part, tell how it works, and explain how it is affected by drugs and alcohol.

Task List	
Partner 1	Be the Brain
Partner 2	Build the Frame

Play the game. Shuffle your deck of ten cards and spread them face down for your partner. Say "Ready, set, concentrate!" and set the timer. Your partner must turn over two cards at random. If the cards do not match, the player puts them face down again and tries two more cards. When there is a match, note the time and write it down. When all the cards are matched, the sum of the five times listed will be that player's ... re.

... reverse roles. Your partner should shuffle and spread the ... deck of ten cards and time you as you make matches. ... nue the play until both players have had three chances ... y. Then compare your times.

... e game with all twenty cards. Spread all the cards face ... Take turns turning over two cards at a time. When you ... match, remove the cards and go again. The player with ... t cards when play ends wins.

PORTFOLIO ASSESSMENT

Choose among the following products students can put in their Portfolios.

- data from activities
- data from Video, Videodisc, or CD-ROM projects
- data from outside research
- integrated curriculum projects
- projects from Investigate Further activities
- results from Think It-Write It activities

Ongoing Assessment Opportunities

	Performance	Portfolio	Written Reviews and Tests
Chapter 1			G23, AG 164–165
Investigation 1	TG G13		G13, AG 162
Investigation 2		TG G22	G22, AG 163
Chapter 2			G45, AG 168–169
Investigation 1		TG G33	G33, AG 166
Investigation 2	TG G44		G44, AG 167
Chapter 3			G63, AG 172–173
Investigation 1		TG G55	G55, AG 170
Investigation 2	TG G62		G62, AG 171
Unit Close	AG 174–175		AG 178–181

Key: TG = Teacher Guide   AG = Assessment Guide   All other pages are from the Student Edition.

Unit Tests

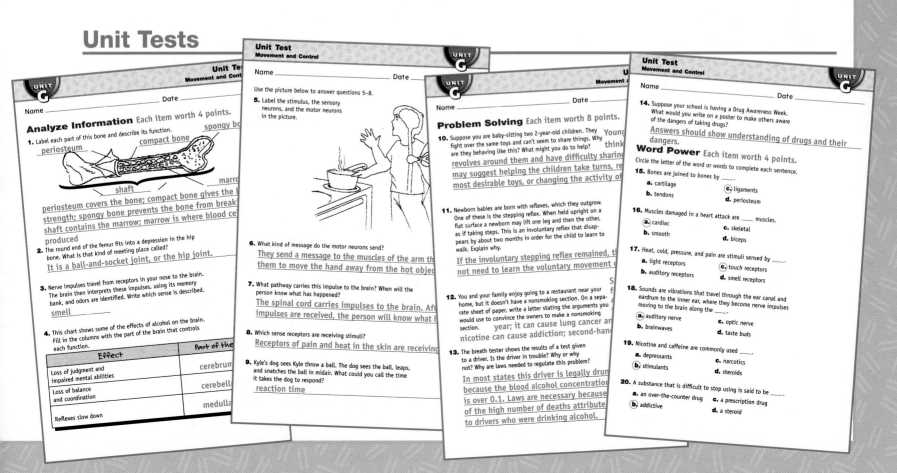

UNIT PROJECT

Matching Bone, Muscle, and Brain Power

Students gain a better understanding of movement and control by planning and coordinating activities that demonstrate how their skeletal, muscular, and nervous systems work together.

Getting Ready

Group Size
4 to 6 students

Have each group work cooperatively to develop competitive athletic events that demonstrate how the skeletal, muscular, and nervous systems work together.

Materials

For Posters and Flowcharts

• Poster board, paints, markers, and so on

For Triathlon

• Starting gun, scoreboard, and various props and equipment

Other Materials

• Unit Project Masters G1–G6, TRB pp. 108–113
• *Science Notebook* pp. 357, 375, 383
• Transparencies 31–35

Plan Ahead

Provide time and space for groups to plan their events and make their posters and flowcharts. Decide where the triathlon will be held.

Building the Project
Through Project Links

Chapter 1, p. G12 Have each group plan a competitive athletic event that demonstrates how bones and muscles work together to cause movement. If you wish, use *Science Notebook* p. 357 to help students with their lists. Each group should also make a poster to show the main bones, muscles, and joints that are involved in the activity. The poster should show which muscles contract and relax to cause movements during the activity.

Assessing Student Progress: Students should be able to explain their posters.

Chapter 2, p. G41 Student groups should each plan a competitive physical activity that demonstrates the coordination of the skeletal and muscular systems by the nervous system. These activities should be something that challenges students, but are still possible to do. Each group should make a flowchart to show the pathways of nerve impulses during its activity. *Science Notebook* p. 375 might be helpful at this time.

Assessing Student Progress: Determine if each group member participates in the planning of the activity and preparation of the flowchart.

Chapter 3, p. G51 Challenge groups to each think of a competitive physical activity, such as a three-legged race, that demonstrates impaired coordination similar to how the body can be affected by the misuse of drugs. These activities should be safe and easy to do. Groups should make up advertising slogans about their activities, warning others of the effects of losing physical control due to drug misuse. Use *Science Notebook* p. 383 to assist students with their lists, if you wish.

Assessing Student Progress: Observe how well each group works together to plan their physical activity and to make their slogan.

Wrapping Up the Project

Bone, Muscle, Brain Triathlon

Have all groups work together to plan a competitive athletic meet—The Bone, Muscle, Brain Triathlon—that will have three categories of events: Movement Events, Coordination Events, and Impaired Coordination Events. Each group should be responsible for one event in each category—these are the activities the groups plan in the Unit Project Links. Each group is responsible for all the props and equipment needed for its events. Before each event, have groups present their posters, flowcharts, or advertising slogans. One member of each group can act as announcer for the group's events. Other group members can demonstrate the activity to contestants and serve as judges for the event. Invite families, friends, and other classes to the triathlon.

OTHER PROJECTS TO DO

- **Publish a Guide.** Investigate exercises that help develop the body's strength and flexibility. Draw pictures to show how these exercises are done properly. Include descriptions to help people understand the benefits of the exercises.

- **Investigate Muscle Pairs.** Identify pairs of muscles and find out how they team up to work together. Measure the strength of some muscles that are paired together. Draw pictures to show how the paired muscles work together. Write descriptions and display them along with the pictures on poster board.

PEOPLE TO CONTACT

In Person

- Contact a physical therapist to describe to the class the treatment plans for patients who have been immobilized or who lack flexibility.

By Mail

- **American Physical Therapy Association,** 111 N. Fairfax Street, Alexandria, VA 22314
- **Aerobics & Fitness Association of America,** 15250 Ventura Blvd., Suite 200, Sherman Oaks, CA 91403

By Computer

- Connect to the *SilverShare Bulletin Board* to exchange data and the results of your investigations with other *Silver Burdett Ginn Science DiscoveryWorks* users. Watch for our Internet address, coming soon!

PLACES TO VISIT

- **Aerobic or fitness centers** may be a source of information on how to enhance the body's movement and adaptability.

- **Athletic events** often showcase participants' graceful body movements and agility.

- **Rehabilitation centers** provide specially equipped facilities that help the body to regain strength and flexibility.

Emergency

Overview This Videodisc module poses a problem for students to solve by asking: Why is it possible to experience a stomachache when responding to an emergency? To solve the problem, students investigate adrenaline, skeletal muscle, and smooth muscle. The first of six segments in the mod- ule introduces the problem. The second, third, and fourth segments present clues students need to solve the problem. The fifth segment suggests a solution. The sixth segment provides a brief extension on a related topic.

Using the Videodisc Module

You can show the module at the beginning of the unit as an opening activity, at the end of the unit as a review, or at the key points listed below.

1. Introducing the Problem

The Opening Segment *(Beginning the Unit)*

The opening scene shows the main character, Sue, who, while playing outside, hears cries for help from her grandmother's apartment. She races up the stairs to find a stove burner on and her grandmother locked in the bathroom. Sue turns off the burner and helps her grandmother, but when all the excitement is over, she is left with a stomachache.

2. Gathering Clues

Segment 2: Adrenaline *(Chapter 2, Inv. 1)*

How does adrenaline affect other parts of the body? Students explore the function of adrenaline, a hormone that is released by the adrenal glands dur- ing emergencies. It causes the heart to beat faster, breathing to increase, and a greater blood flow to the brain and certain muscles, while decreasing blood flow to other muscles.

Segment 3: Skeletal Muscles *(Chapter 1, Inv. 2)*

How are skeletal muscles used for moving the body? Students learn that skeletal muscles are attached to bones by tendons. When skeletal muscles contract, they cause tendons to pull on the bones. Skeletal muscles get their energy from food and oxygen.

Segment 4: Smooth Muscle *(Chapter 1, Inv. 2)*

How does food move through the digestive sys- tem? Students learn that contractions of smooth mus- cle that line the esophagus, stomach, and intestines move food through these organs. Contractions and movement of food are slowed if blood flow decreases to smooth muscle. Food that stays in the digestive sys- tem too long can cause a stomachache.

3. Exploring a Solution

Students work independently, in groups, or as a class to develop a solution to the problem of why a person may experience a stomachache when responding to an emergency.

Segment 5: The Solution *(End of Unit)*

After constructing a solution of their own, students watch and discuss the solution presented in Segment 5. The solution explains that in an emergency, adrenaline is released and redistributes the flow of blood in the body. To make more blood available to skeletal muscles, less blood is sent to the digestive system. As a result, the digestive system slows, which may cause a stomachache.

4. Extending

Segment 6: Additional Information

Students learn more about the human body through labeled diagrams of these systems: circulatory, diges- tive, respiratory, muscular, skeletal, excretory, ner- vous, endocrine, and reproductive.

Using the Tools

The CD-ROM includes on-screen tools that can help students report results of activities, produce reports, or organize data.

Spreadsheet   Students can use this tool to chart and record the length of arm muscles in the Chapter 1 Push or Pull? activity and the times recorded for the Test Your Mind activity in Chapter 2. They can also chart the results of their survey in Chapter 3.

Grapher   After entering their data in a Spreadsheet, students may want to create a bar graph to show the class results of the response time activity in Chapter 2.

Writer   Students can record their observations of bones and muscles in the Chapter 1 activities, and balance and reaction time activities in Chapter 2. They may also use this tool to write their survey questions for the Ad Power activity and to describe the results of their debate in Chapter 3.

Painter   Students can draw and label features of bones in Chapter 1 activities.

Calculator   Students can use this tool to make comparisons of Chapter 2 response time results.

Timer   Students can use this tool to time the Tired Muscles activity in Chapter 1, and the Measuring Response Time and Test Your Mind activities in Chapter 2.

OTHER TECHNOLOGY RESOURCES

Videos

Your Active Body: Bones and Movement*   Students learn about bones and ligaments, how joints work, and how broken bones heal. Use with Chapter 1.

Your Active Body: Muscles and Energy*   Students learn about the structure and function of muscles and the relationship between muscles and energy. Use with Chapter 1.

The Dare to Be Aware Series*   Students observe the damaging effects that drugs and alcohol have on the lives of several teenagers. Use with Chapter 3.

*Available from Silver Burdett Ginn

UNIT G

Movement and Control

GET READY TO INVESTIGATE!

Overview

In this unit, students will learn about the skeletal and muscular systems and will discover how bones and muscles cause movement. They will also study the nervous system and how various drugs affect the body.

Warming Up

As students look at pages G2–G3, stimulate discussion with these questions:

- **What do you see in the first column photograph? What connections do you think there might be between mind and body?**

- **What do you think the students in the photograph in the second column are doing? How can experimenting with models and hypothesizing help us discover how bones move at a joint?**

- Point out the book cover to students and invite them to read the summaries. The book pictured is in the Trade Book Library. **How do you think technology helps train Olympic athletes?**

- **What are the students in the last photograph doing? As we work through this unit, think about some ways you can apply what you learn about movement and control to plan a Bone, Muscle, Brain Triathlon sports event.**

 Have students use *Science Notebook* p. 349.

G 2

GET READY TO

OBSERVE & QUESTION

How can you respond to things around you?

What if there was a wheelchair that could be completely controlled by a disabled person's brain waves? Learn how scientists are making connections between mind and body by using new technologies.

EXPERIMENT & HYPOTHESIZE

What are the parts of the skeletal system?

Make a bone model and discover how bones move at a joint. Can you predict where each type of joint is found in your body? Check out your predictions with a model of the human skeleton.

G2

Home-School Connection

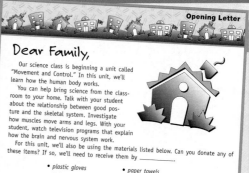

The Opening Letter at the beginning of the unit introduces family members to the skeletal, muscular, and nervous systems. Distribute the Opening Letter (TRB p. 33) at the start of the unit.

Dear Family,

Our science class is beginning a unit called "Movement and Control." In this unit, we'll learn how the human body works.

You can help bring science from the classroom to your home. Talk with your student about the relationship between good posture and the skeletal system. Investigate how muscles move arms and legs. With your student, watch television programs that explain how the brain and nervous system work.

For this unit, we'll also be using the materials listed below. Can you donate any of these items? If so, we'll need to receive them by _____

- *plastic gloves*
- *index cards*
- *old magazines*
- *paper towels*
- *posterboard*

Do you or other family members have a special interest in body systems? Could you help with activities? If so, please fill out the form below and have your student return it to class.

Thank you for your help!

Opening Letter
Movement and Control

Your name _____ Student's name _____

Home phone _____ Work phone _____

INVESTIGATE!

RESEARCH & ANALYZE

As you investigate, find out more from these books.

- **Peak Performance** by Emily Isberg (Simon & Schuster Books for Young Readers, 1989). Discover how up-to-the-minute scientific technology helps athletes all over the world. Read about the workings of the U.S. Olympic Training Centers.

- **Native American Doctor: The Story of Susan LaFlesche Picotte** by Jeri Ferris (Carolrhoda Books, 1991). This biography takes you to the Great Plains in the 1860's. Learn how alcohol abuse was fought by the first Native American woman to earn a medical degree.

WORK TOGETHER & SHARE IDEAS

What's your plan for a sports event that involves three systems of your body?

You'll design a series of activities to show how your skeletal, muscular, and nervous systems all work together. Have fun planning and competing in your Bone, Muscle, Brain Triathlon!

G3

Triathlon

Additional Student Resources

Movement by Jenny Bryan (Dillon Press, 1992). How the parts of the body work together to allow movement. **(Text Correlation: Chapter 1)**

The Story of My Life by Helen Keller (Scholastic, 1967). The autobiography of a woman who excelled in spite of her blindness and deafness. **(Text Correlation: Chapter 2)**

Your Two Brains by Patricia Stafford (Atheneum, 1986). Illustrated with black-and-white drawings, this is a clear explanation of the differences between the left and right sides of the brain. **(Text Correlation: Chapter 2)**

BOOKS AND ARTICLES FOR TEACHERS

The Brain and Nervous System by Mark Lambert (Silver Burdett, 1988). Thorough coverage with information about the brain, spinal cord, nervous system, senses, hormones, chemical messengers, intelligence, and memory.

The Downside of Drugs by Regina Avraham (Chelsea House, 1988). An informative overview of drugs—nicotine, alcohol, narcotics, stimulants, depressants, hallucinogens—and their effect on the individual and society.

"Gray Matters" by Sharon Begley (*Newsweek*, March 27, 1995). New technologies that catch the brain in the act of thinking, feeling, and remembering reveal differences in ways men and women use their brains. Interesting findings reach no conclusion as to the cause—biological or environmental—of these differences.

How the Body Works by Steve Parker (Reader's Digest Association, 1994). Experiments and information promote discovery and learning about the skeletal structure, body movement, nervous system, and the brain. An excellent collection of experiments related to the human body.

Messengers to the Brain: Our Fantastic Five Senses by Paul D. Martin (National Geographic Society, 1984). Spectacular photographs and diagrams show the brain and map the nervous system throughout the body as well as providing a detailed description of each sense and how it works.

Science Projects About the Human Body by Robert Gardner (Enslow Publishers, 1993). Activities that investigate and promote learning about the human body, including bones, muscles, and senses. Simple experiments that use available materials.

Subconcepts	Activities	Materials

Investigation 1 What Are the Parts of the Skeletal System?

The skeletal system, which supports and protects other body parts, is made up of many bones, together with the tissues that protect them; bones meet at movable and immovable joints. *Suggested Pacing: 2–3 class periods* **Standards** p. 156	**A Closer Look at Bones,** p. G6 *Science Processes:* observe, classify, communicate, infer	goggles*, gloves*, paper towels, hand lens*, bone specimen, *Science Notebook* pp. 353–354
	Where Bones Meet, p. G7 *Science Processes:* observe; classify; infer; predict; collect, record, and interpret data; make and use models	bone diagrams, scissors, tape, posterboard, paste, brass fastener*, model of a human skeleton*, Activity Support Master G1 (TRB p. 64) *Science Notebook* p. 355

Investigation 2 How Do Bones and Muscles Cause Movement?

Muscles contract and pull on bones, causing them to bend at joints and achieve movement; many injuries to bones and muscles can be avoided by taking precautions. *Suggested Pacing: 2–3 class periods* **Standards** pp. 156, 168	**Push or Pull?,** p. G14 *Science Processes:* observe; measure; communicate; infer; collect, record, and interpret data; define operationally; make hypotheses; make and use models	tape measure*, *Science Notebook* pp. 359–360
	Tired Muscles, p. G16 *Science Processes*: observe; measure; infer; collect, record, and interpret data; identify and control variables; experiment	spring clip, timer*, *Science Notebook* p. 361

Overview

In this chapter students explore two important systems of the human body—the skeletal system and the muscular system—and discover how bones and muscles work together to cause movement.

Chapter Concept

The skeletal system and the muscular system each have their own functions and also work together to allow body movement.

Advance Preparation	Curriculum Connection	Assessment
A Closer Look at Bones Obtain beef, pork, or lamb bones from a butcher and have the bones cut lengthwise or in cross section so students can observe the inside structure. Larger grocery-store chains may provide quantities of bones for classroom use at little or no cost. **Where Bones Meet** None	Language Arts TG p. G8 Integrating the Sciences TG p. G10 Cultural Connection TG p. G11	**Chapter 1 Baseline Assessment:** *Science Notebook* pp. 351–352 **Investigation 1 Baseline Assessment:** TG p. G6 **Investigation 1 Review:** AG p. 162 **Think It/Write It,** p. G13; *Science Notebook* p. 358 **Following Up on Baseline Assessment:** TG p. G13 **Performance:** TG p. G13
Push or Pull? None **Tired Muscles** None	Language Arts TG p. G17 Integrating the Sciences TG p. G18 Cultural Connection TG p. G19 Math TG p. G20 Literature TG p. G21 Science, Technology, & Society TG p. G21	**Investigation 2 Baseline Assessment:** TG p. G14 **Investigation 2 Review:** AG p. 163 **Think It/Write It,** p. G22; *Science Notebook* p. 362 **Following Up on Baseline Assessment:** TG p. G22 **Portfolio:** TG p. G22 **Chapter 1 Summative Assessment** Reflect and Evaluate, p. G23 Chapter 1 Review/Test: AG pp. 164–165 *Science Notebook* pp. 363–364

TG= Teaching Guide   TRB= Teacher Resource Book   AG= Assessment Guide   *Materials in Equipment Kit

Introducing the Chapter

Chapter Overview

Chapter Concept The skeletal system and the muscular system each have their own functions but also work together to allow body movement.

Theme: Systems

The interaction between two important systems—the muscular system and the skeletal system—allows the body to move and to work.

Common Misconceptions

Students may think that bones are used only to move the body from place to place. This chapter also points out the protective role carried out by some parts of the skeletal system, especially the ribs and skull.

Options for Setting the Stage

Warm-Up Activity

Challenge students to write their names in the air without moving a muscle. They will not be able to comply. Repeat the same request, but this time tell students to move the necessary muscles. Ask them which bones were involved in the motion.

Use *Science Notebook* pp. 351–352.

Discussion Starter:
Will I Walk Again?

Use the photo and text to start a discussion about rehabilitation after a spinal injury.

- **Dennis Byrd had not injured his hands. Why would he be unable to unsnap his helmet?** The message from Byrd's brain could not reach his hands because he had injured his spinal cord.

- **Byrd's legs were not injured either. Why could he not walk after the injury?** The injury prevented messages from his brain from reaching his legs.

- **Career:** *Physical Therapist*
  Although many thought Byrd would never walk again, one important factor was the work of physical therapists who flexed and stretched his motionless limbs when he was unable to move. Physical therapists have a college degree in physical therapy.

CHAPTER 1

BONES AND MUSCLES

Watch the ways athletes move. They use their legs to run and jump in the air. They use their hands to catch balls of different shapes. It's a blur of motion. What systems of the body allow for these amazing movements? How do these systems work together?

Will I Walk Again?

In 1992, New York Jets defensive lineman 270-lb Dennis Byrd collided with a 275-lb teammate on the field. Byrd shattered a vertebra, one of the 33 bones of the spine. This caused injury to the nerve tissue of the spinal cord. The muscles in his arms and legs didn't work, and Dennis Byrd couldn't move.

"Am I going to be paralyzed?" Byrd kept asking. The Jets team doctor feared that the answer would be "Yes." But Dennis Byrd was determined not to give up. Two weeks after extensive surgery on his spine, he began physical therapy. At first, therapists had to move Byrd's limbs for him. But after several weeks of intensive exercises, he was not only moving his limbs on his own but was racing around in a wheelchair. Gradually, Dennis Byrd learned to walk again.

In this chapter you'll learn how the bones and muscles of the body make walking and other movements possible.

G4

Home-School Connection

In the Explore at Home activity "Bones and Muscles," students compare the bones and muscles of a chicken wing with the human arm. Distribute the activity (TRB p. 33) when students have completed the chapter. Ask what systems students use to raise their hands in class.

Opening Letter

Dear Family,

Our science class is beginning a unit called "Movement and Control." In this unit, we'll learn how the human body works.

You can help bring science from the classroom to your home. Talk with your student about the relationship between good posture and the skeletal system. Investigate how muscles move arms and legs. With your student, watch television programs that explain how the brain and nervous system work.

For this unit, we'll also be using the materials listed below. Can you donate any of these items? If so, we'll need to receive them by _____.

- plastic gloves
- index cards
- old magazines
- paper towels
- posterboard

Do you or other family members have a special interest in body systems? Could you help with activities? If so, please fill out the form below and have your student return it to class.

Thank you for your help!

Opening Letter
Movement and Control

Your name _____ Student's name _____

Home phone _____ Work phone _____

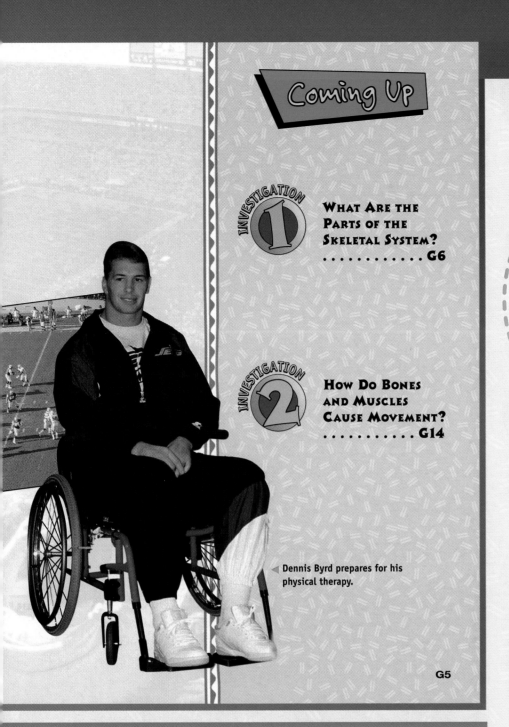

Coming Up

WHAT ARE THE PARTS OF THE SKELETAL SYSTEM?
.... G6

HOW DO BONES AND MUSCLES CAUSE MOVEMENT?
.... G14

◄ Dennis Byrd prepares for his physical therapy.

G5

Technology Alert

Videodisc

Emergency Opening Segment and Segments 3–5

In *Emergency*, students will evaluate a hypothetical situation in which a girl responds to a cry for help and later experiences a stomachache. In the opening segment, students observe Sue reacting to her grandmother's cries for help. Although the situation results in no injuries or damage, Sue experiences an upset stomach when the excitement is over. In segment 3, students learn about the structure and function of skeletal muscles. Segment 4 explains how smooth muscles function. In segment 5, students speculate about why a person might experience a stomachache when responding to an emergency and compare their suggestions with that presented in the segment.

Chapter Road Map

What Are the Parts of the Skeletal System?

Activities	Resources
A Closer Look at Bones	✳ Bone Basics
✳ Where Bones Meet	✳ What Kind of Joint Is This?

How Do Bones and Muscles Cause Movement?

Activities	Resources
✳ Push or Pull?	✳ How Do Muscles Work?
Tired Muscles	Avoiding Bone and Muscle Injuries

✳Pressed for Time?

As you work through the upcoming investigations, focus on the activities and resources identified by the clock.

 Look for this symbol in front of questions that help develop Scientific Reasoning Skills.

WHAT ARE THE PARTS OF THE SKELETAL SYSTEM?

Planner

Subconcept The skeletal system, which supports and protects other body parts, is made up of many bones, together with the tissues that protect them; bones meet at movable and immovable joints.

Objectives

- **Observe** bone specimens, **record** observations, and **draw conclusions** about bone.
- **List** the functions of the skeletal system.
- **Investigate** how joints allow movement.

Pacing 2–3 class periods

Science Terms bone, skeletal system, joint, ligaments, cartilage

Activate Prior Knowledge

Baseline Assessment Ask: **What would you look like without bones?** Have students draw their responses. Save the drawings for use in Following Up.

Activity A Closer Look at Bones

Preview *Students focus on a bone specimen and should conclude that bone is made up of both living and nonliving material.*

Advance Preparation *See p. G4b.*

1. Get Ready

Time about 30 minutes

Grouping pairs

Collaborative Strategy One student might record data while the other observes the characteristics of the specimen. You may wish to provide the Activity Support Master "Compare–Contrast Diagram" (TRB p. 68).

Safety Review safety precautions with students. Remind students to wear gloves during the activity and wash their hands afterwards.

How many bones do you think make up the human skeleton? Would you say 50? 100? You might be surprised to learn that the human skeleton has 206 bones! These range from the long bone in your thigh to the tiny bones in your ears. Find out more about your skeletal system in Investigation 1.

Activity

A Closer Look at Bones

Although you have a full set of bones, you really can't study them. But in this activity you'll get a chance to look closely at a bone.

MATERIALS
- goggles
- gloves
- paper towels
- hand lens
- bone specimen
- *Science Notebook*

SAFETY
Wear goggles and gloves when handling the bone specimen.

Procedure

Observe the outside covering and features of the bone. Describe the bone in your *Science Notebook*. Next, observe the inside of the bone. Notice how the inside structure differs from the outside structure. Describe the inside of the bone. Make a drawing of the bone. Talk with your group. What can you infer about the material that makes up the bone?

Analyze and Conclude

1. Compare and contrast the inside structure of the bone with the outside structure of the bone.

2. Do you think that bones are living material? What evidence supports your conclusion?

G6

---

2. Guide the Procedure

Students may record their observations and inferences, and answer questions on *Science Notebook* pp. 353–354.

You may wish to have students use the CD-ROM Painter to display their observations.

3. Assess Performance

Process Skills Checklist

- Did students accurately **compare** and **contrast** the specimen's interior and exterior structures?
- Did students **infer** that bone is made up of both living and nonliving matter?

Analyze and Conclude

1. The outside of bone is porous, relatively smooth, and hard. The inside contains soft tissue and blood vessels.

2. The presence of blood vessels indicates that the inner part of bone is made of living material.

Activity

Where Bones Meet

What would happen if all of your bones were fixed in place? How would you move? Find out what structures allow movement of your skeleton.

MATERIALS
- bone diagrams
- scissors
- tape
- posterboard
- paste
- brass fastener
- model of a human skeleton
- *Science Notebook*

Procedure

1. Work with a partner. Cut out the bone diagrams and tape them together to form two long bones. Paste the bones on posterboard and cut them out.

2. Use a fastener to attach an end of one bone to an end of the other bone. **Observe** the ways in which the bones of your model move. **Describe** in your *Science Notebook* how the bones move.

3. **Predict** where in the human skeleton bones move in a similar way to your model. **Record** your predictions.

4. **Examine** your own body or a model of a human skeleton to find places where bones move in a similar way to your model. **Record** these places.

Step 2

Analyze and Conclude

1. **Compare** your observations of your skeleton or the human skeleton model with your predictions. How are they alike? How do they differ?

2. The place where two bones meet is called a joint. What can you **infer** about the functions of joints?

3. Did you find additional bones in your body or in the skeleton model moving like your long-bone model? Where were they located?

4. How did bones in your body move differently from your model?

G7

Responding to Individual Needs

Inclusion Activity To ensure that students understand that their model represents a joint, have them locate a movable joint on both their paper models and their own bodies. Help them to use an encyclopedia to find out the names of the bones that meet to form the joint. Have them label the two bones on their paper models, as well as the joint.

Visual/Spatial Activity To expand the activity, use **Transparency 32**, "Joints," to show students the various types of joints found in the human skeleton, also presented on pp. G12–G13.

Activity Where Bones Meet

Preview *Students focus on movement of the human skeleton and should infer that joints allow movement of the body.*

1. Get Ready

Time about 30 minutes

Grouping pairs

Collaborative Strategy One student might be responsible for manipulating the posterboard model, while the other finds corresponding movements on the human skeletal model.

Materials Hints Use Activity Support Master G1 (TRB p. 64).

Safety Review safety precautions with students. Remind students to exercise caution when cutting out and fastening their "bones" together.

2. Guide the Procedure

- Encourage students to observe and record the movement of joints in the skeleton that may move in different ways than the joint in their long-bone model.

Students may record information and answer questions on *Science Notebook* p. 355.

You may wish to have students use the CD-ROM Spreadsheet to organize and display their data.

3. Assess Performance

Process Skills Checklist
- Did students accurately **make a model** of a joint?
- Did students accurately **observe** and **record** the joints of the human skeleton?
- Did students **infer** that joints enable the skeleton to move?

Analyze and Conclude
1. Students may respond that bones at the elbow, knee, fingers, and toes move like the model, but other body parts, such as the neck, hip, and ankle, move differently.
2. Joints permit movement of the skeleton.
3. Answers will vary with students' predictions.
4. Students' responses will vary.

Bone Basics

Preview *Students focus on the components, structure, and functions of the skeletal system.*

1. Get Ready

Science Terms bone, skeletal system, joint, ligaments, cartilage

Background

• Bone, unlike other living tissues of the body, is characterized by dense deposits of calcium. Thus, in addition to living tissue, bone is the body's calcium storage depository. The calcium deposits provide bone with its strength and account for more than half of its mass. When the body has sufficient calcium for its needs, calcium is retained in the bones. When the body's calcium needs are not supplied by diet, calcium from the bones is released for use elsewhere in the body. Calcium-rich foods include low-fat dairy products, broccoli, and canned sardines and anchovies.

• There are two types of bone marrow: yellow marrow and red marrow. It is the red marrow that produces red blood cells, lymphocytes—a type of white blood cell, and platelets.

Discussion Starter

• **What do bones do?** Students might respond that they form the skeleton, permit movement, support the body, and protect inner organs.

• **How do bones allow the body to move?** Bones meet at joints, which allow movement.

• **How do bones protect the body?** Bones protect inner organs by surrounding them. **Which bones do you think have the most important job of protecting the body?** The skull protects the brain, and the ribs protect the heart, lungs, and other vital organs.

Bone Basics

◄ **What's missing that could turn this blob into a human being?**

Think of yourself as a blob, squirming around beneath your desk. Your eyes, ears, nose, and mouth sit generally atop your body, which looks something like a balloon filled with jelly. Your stomach, lungs, liver, and heart are floating in there somewhere, though in no particular place. Forget about arms and legs—you're just a lumpy mass of guts plopped on the floor.

Now that's a scary thought! What could be added to this blob that would transform it into the stunning person you are? Bones, of course! And those bones wouldn't just be thrown in there anywhere. They would have to be organized into an appropriate system that would give your body protection, shape, and the ability to move.

The Skeletal System

A **bone** is a kind of body tissue made of both living cells and nonliving material. Each human body contains 206 different bones. All the bones in the body, together with tissues that bind and protect the bones, form the **skeletal system**, or the skeleton.

Have you ever done a jigsaw puzzle?

The pieces fit together so perfectly that no glue is needed and no gaps are seen in the completed picture. Most bones of the skeleton don't fit together in such a perfect fashion. And unlike a jigsaw puzzle, a skeleton has to stay together when you run or jump or move.

The place at which two bones meet is called a **joint**. Some joints, such as those in the skull, are almost like the pieces of a jigsaw puzzle. But at many joints—the elbows, knees, wrists, and others—movement occurs. At these joints the bones are held in place by strong bands of fiber called **ligaments**. Ligaments allow some movement while keeping the bones generally in place.

Bones are protected at joints by **cartilage**, a tissue much like bone but softer and more flexible. Cartilage is also found in the nose, the ears, and the tip of the breastbone. It forms part of the skeletal system.

G8

Integrating the Curriculum

Science & Language Arts

EXPRESSIONS **What to Do** Encourage students to list at least five expressions that are related to the skeletal system and to speculate about the origins of the sayings. For example, "getting off on the wrong foot" has its origin in ancient Rome, where superstition held that it was bad luck to enter a house with the left foot first. Other expressions that students might think of include "using elbow grease," "knuckling under," and "being all thumbs."

What's the Result? Students can display the common expressions along with whimsical illustrations on posterboard to share with the class.

Multi-Age Classroom Students might enjoy working in small groups to think of expressions related to the skeletal system. A student who is adept at writing could record the expressions.

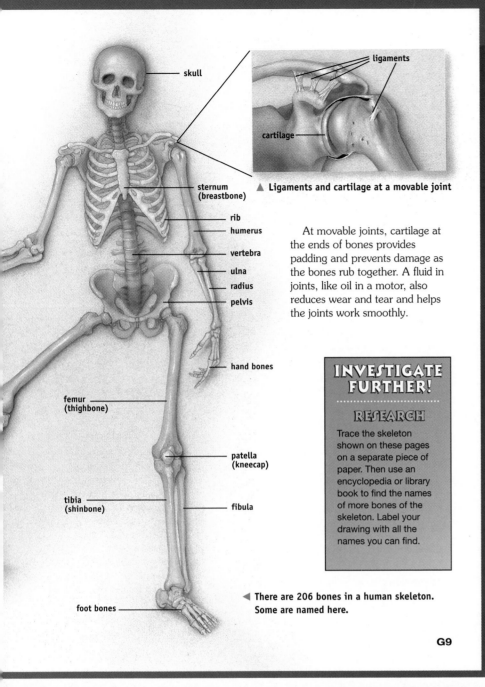

skull

ligaments

cartilage

▲ Ligaments and cartilage at a movable joint

sternum
(breastbone)

rib

humerus

vertebra

ulna

radius

pelvis

hand bones

femur
(thighbone)

patella
(kneecap)

tibia
(shinbone)

fibula

foot bones

At movable joints, cartilage at the ends of bones provides padding and prevents damage as the bones rub together. A fluid in joints, like oil in a motor, also reduces wear and tear and helps the joints work smoothly.

INVESTIGATE FURTHER!

RESEARCH

Trace the skeleton shown on these pages on a separate piece of paper. Then use an encyclopedia or library book to find the names of more bones of the skeleton. Label your drawing with all the names you can find.

◀ There are 206 bones in a human skeleton. Some are named here.

G9

Investigate Further

Research

Encourage students to make their drawings on p. 356 of their *Science Notebooks*. Accept all reasonable efforts to label skeleton drawings.
🔲 **The medical specialty that has to do with diseases and injuries involving bones is called orthopedics. What might you like about being an orthopedic surgeon?** Students might like the feeling of being able to diagnose and treat people, and helping them to recover from bone injury or disease.

Choose from the following strategies to facilitate discussion.

Making Comparisons

- **How are bones and cartilage different?** Cartilage is a smooth, flexible material. Bone is more rigid and contains more minerals than cartilage. **How are they similar?** Both substances support and shape the body.

Thinking Critically

🔲 **Move your wrists, elbows, shoulders, knees, and ankles in as many directions as possible. How can you tell if joints are present at each of these parts of your body?** Students should realize these parts of the body are where two bones meet and are held together in a reasonably stable position. **How might you know if they are the same types of joints?** Help students understand that there are different types of joints that allow different types of movement. Students should realize by demonstrating the movements, for example, that the elbow allows a different type of movement than the wrist.

Responding to Individual Needs

Visual/Spatial Activity To help students visualize the bones in the human skeleton, you may wish to use **Transparency 31,** "The Skeleton."

Connecting to the Activities

- **A Closer Look at Bones, p. G6**
  When you examined a bone, what parts did you see? Students should respond that they saw compact bone, spongy bone, and marrow. Depending on the bones used, periosteum may also have been present.

- **What are the functions of each part of the bone?** Compact bone gives bone its strength. Spongy bone protects the bone from breaking by acting like a shock absorber. Bone marrow produces blood cells.

Drawing Conclusions

The body stores its calcium in bones. What might happen if your body got an insufficient supply of calcium? Guide students to conclude that their bones could weaken if their calcium intake is insufficient, because calcium is leached from bone for other uses in the body.

Identifying and Solving Problems

- **If bones are broken or damaged in other ways, the body becomes injured. This is most serious when the head is involved. How can you help prevent head injuries?** Students might respond that during certain activities, they can protect against head injuries by wearing helmets. **For what activities might you want to wear a protective helmet?** Answers might include cycling, in-line skating, and ice skating.

Why might a person choose not to wear a helmet while involved in a potentially dangerous activity? Students might say that the person didn't expect to get hurt or doesn't want the bother or expense of a helmet.

Inside a Bone

A bone has a complex structure, as you discovered in the activity on page G6. Bone isn't just a nonliving building material. A typical long bone, such as the one pictured at right, is enlarged at both ends with a shaft in between. A membrane called the periosteum (per ē-äs'tē əm) covers the bone. Under the periosteum is a layer of very hard material called compact bone. This layer gives the bone its strength.

Beneath the layer of compact bone is a material called spongy bone. Spongy bone is softer than compact bone and contains many hollow spaces. Those spaces help prevent the bone from breaking, because they act as shock absorbers when the bone is hit or banged. Spongy bone makes up most of the material at the ends of long bones.

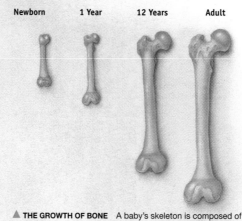

periosteum

compact bone

spongy bone

Newborn   **1 Year**   **12 Years**   **Adult**

▲ **THE GROWTH OF BONE** A baby's skeleton is composed of cartilage. As a baby grows into a child and then an adult, most of the cartilage is gradually replaced by bone.

Inside the shaft of long bones is a soft tissue called marrow. This is where the body's blood cells are produced. The blood cells leave the bone through blood vessels that weave their way throughout the bone. Like other living tissues in your body, your bones must be supplied with blood or they will die.

G10

Investigate Further

Integrating the Sciences

PHYSICAL SCIENCE

What to Do Students can investigate the effects of calcium withdrawal on bone strength by placing uncooked chicken bones in vinegar for about 36 hours. Students should wear plastic gloves when handling the bones, and goggles when using the vinegar. **What's the Result? What happened to the bone when it was soaked in vinegar?** It became soft and rubbery. **Why do you think this happened?** Students should infer that the bone became soft because the calcium was drawn out of it by the vinegar. **Under what circumstances do you think this could happen in your body?** Bones could weaken if insufficient calcium is taken in.
Multi-Age Classroom While some students write their observations, others can research sources of dietary calcium.

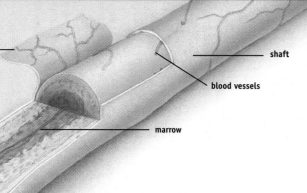

shaft

blood vessels

marrow

A bone is living tissue with a complex structure.

A System That Supports and Protects

Without a skeletal system, you would be just a blob, like the one described on page G8. Your skeleton gives you your shape. It supports your other body parts and allows you to stand erect. With your bones and their joints, you can move around and do many amazing things.

Your skeleton also serves you in another important way. It protects the soft organs within your body. Could you live long without a barrier around your lungs, heart, and liver? The ribs provide that barrier, giving protection against the hard knocks that you experience every day. Can you think of other bones that protect soft organs? ∎

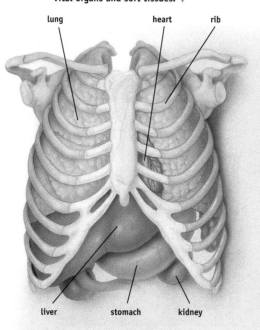

Part of the skeleton, the ribs protect vital organs and soft tissues. ▼

lung   heart   rib

liver   stomach   kidney

G11

Making Inferences

- **What do you think might happen if your ribs or skull were broken?** Students should infer that broken ribs might injure the heart, liver, or lungs, and that a broken skull could damage the brain.
- **What other bones protect soft organs?** The pelvis protects reproductive organs, and the vertebrae protect the spinal cord.

Drawing Conclusions

- **How can you help make sure that your bones remain healthy throughout your life?** Answers might include eating a diet that provides the nutrients necessary for bone growth and maintenance, and following a regimen of moderate exercise. Students might also mention that they could avoid toxins such as radiation and that exposure to sunlight can help prevent vitamin D deficiency.

Thinking About the Data

- **As the diagram on p. G11 suggests, your rib cage surrounds and protects important organs and soft tissues. Try to feel the outline of your rib cage.** Explain that students may be better able to feel the outline of their ribs by placing their fingers on their sides and working towards the middle. **Can you count your ribs?** Answers will vary. **What happens to your ribs as you inhale and exhale?** Students should realize that as they inhale the rib cage contracts and that as they exhale the rib cage expands. **Why do you think this is important?** Students should conclude that this ability allows space for the lungs to take in air as they breathe.

🔵 Responding to Individual Needs

Students Acquiring English Have students make drawings of a long bone, as shown on these two pages. As they label the drawing in English, help them pronounce the names of the parts.

3. Assess Understanding

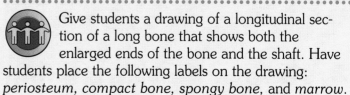

Give students a drawing of a longitudinal section of a long bone that shows both the enlarged ends of the bone and the shaft. Have students place the following labels on the drawing: *periosteum, compact bone, spongy bone,* and *marrow.*

What Kind of Joint Is This?

Preview *Students focus on the different ways joints permit movement of the skeleton.*

1. Get Ready

Background

- Although the skeleton is composed of rigid bones, the human body can move in thousands of different ways. The ability to move is provided by ligaments that hold bones together for both a tight fit and mobility.

- Other joints on the skeleton are the saddle joint, which allows for movement in two planes, and the ellipsoid joints, which permit hinge-type movement.

Discussion Starter

 What would your life be like if your bones weren't connected by joints? Students' bodies would be supported and their organs protected, but they would be unable to perform many activities.

2. Guide the Discussion

Choose from the following strategies to facilitate discussion.

Connecting to the Activities

- ***Where Bones Meet, p. G7***
  When you made a model of a joint, what was missing for normal joint function? Ligaments

Responding to Individual Needs

Kinesthetic Activity Students can manipulate and observe the joints of a skeleton model. **Transparency 32**, "Joints," will aid students in understanding joint types.

3. Assess Understanding

Divide the class into four groups and assign each group one of the joint types. Encourage groups to devise a method of communicating how its joint works. Suggest that they make models.

What Kind of Joint Is This?

 In the activity on page G7, you identified places in the skeletal system where bones fit together—the joints. In fact, you identified movable joints, those that allow for the movement of bones. The body also contains immovable joints, places where bones come together but there is no movement. The best examples of immovable joints are the ones in the skull. There is no reason for these joints to move, since the purpose of the skull is to protect the brain.

As you learned when you read about the human skeletal system on page G8, movable joints are held together by ligaments. The ligaments allow some movement, but not enough so that a joint slips apart. Joints give you the freedom to move your body. A skeleton without joints would be like a statue.

You may have noticed that different joints allow different kinds of movement. Think of how the elbow moves. Compare that with how the shoulder moves. The elbow's movements are limited, while the shoulder has a much wider range of motion. The difference in how these two joints function is the result of their different structures. That is, they are different kinds of joints.

What joints does the soccer player on page G13 use to kick the ball? Without these different kinds of joints, the actions would be impossible!

UNIT PROJECT LINK

As you continue learning about bones and muscles, plan an athletic event that you feel demonstrates how your bones and muscles work together to cause movement. Make a poster to show the main bones, muscles, and joints that are involved in the activity. On your poster, show which muscles contract and relax to cause movements during the activity.

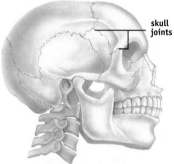

skull joints

▲ The bones of the skull come together at immovable joints.

G12

Investigate Further

Unit Project Link

Students may come up with a wide array of athletic events. They may devise an athletic competition or focus on individual events. Groups of students should design a poster showing the main bones, muscles, and joints involved. Accept reasonable answers that indicate students understand which types of muscles and joints are involved in the activity and which muscles contract and relax to cause the movement. **How does the athletic activity you have chosen help strengthen bones and muscles?** Accept reasonable answers. Have students use p. 357 of their *Science Notebooks* and Unit Project Masters G1–G3 (TRB pp. 108–110).

BALL-AND-SOCKET JOINT This joint allows a great range of motion. In the hip it allows the player to make a full swing of his leg to kick the ball. The same kind of joint is used in a car's gearshift and for the joystick of some games.

PIVOT JOINT A pivot joint in the neck lets the player turn his head to follow the path of the ball after he kicks it.

HINGE JOINT This joint works like a door's hinge. In the knee, it lets the lower leg move back and forth like a door opening and closing. This hinge joint allows the player to pull back his lower leg to kick the ball.

GLIDING JOINT This joint also allows a great range of motion. In a gliding joint, one bone slides over another. This gliding joint in the ankle allows the player to snap his foot into the ball.

─── **INVESTIGATION 1** ───

THINK IT WRITE IT

1. Describe the structure of bones and explain how they are held together to form the skeletal system.

2. You've learned about four different types of movable joints and have an example of each. Now classify other joints in your body by type.

G13

Assessment

Performance

Songs Remind students of the old song "Dem Bones," playing a recording of it if possible. Have students work in small groups to write original lyrics describing how bones are joined by ligaments to form joints. Allow each group to perform its song for the class.

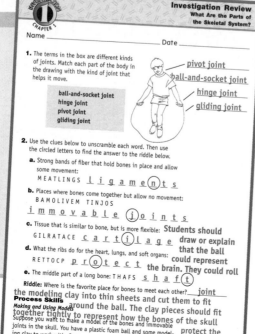

Investigation Review
What Are the Parts of the Skeletal System?

Name _____ Date _____

1. The terms in the box are different kinds of joints. Match each part of the body in the drawing with the kind of joint that helps it move.

ball-and-socket joint
hinge joint
pivot joint
gliding joint

pivot joint
ball-and-socket joint
hinge joint
gliding joint

2. Use the clues below to unscramble each word. Then use the circled letters to find the answer to the riddle below.

a. Strong bands of fiber that hold bones in place and allow some movement:
MEATLINGS l i g a m e n t s

b. Places where bones come together but allow no movement:
BAMOLIVEM TINJOS
i m m o v a b l e j o i n t s

c. Tissue that is similar to bone, but is more flexible:
GILRATACE c a r t i l a g e

d. What the ribs do for the heart, lungs, and soft organs:
RETTOCP p r o t e c t

e. The middle part of a long bone: THAFS s h a f t

Riddle: Where is the favorite place for bones to meet each other? _joint_

Process Skills
Making and Using Models Suppose you want to make a model of the bones and immovable joints in the skull. You have a plastic foam ball and some modeling clay to work with. On a separate sheet of paper, draw or write how you would show how the bones of the skull protect the brain.

Students should draw or explain that the ball could represent the brain. They could roll the modeling clay into thin sheets and cut them to fit together tightly to represent how the bones of the skull protect the brain.

Close the Investigation

THINK IT WRITE IT

Critical Thinking Processes
Analyzing, Applying

1. A typical long bone is a long shaft that is enlarged at both ends. The bone is covered with a membrane, the periosteum. Compact bone lies beneath the periosteum, giving the bone its strength. Under the compact bone, at the enlarged ends, is a material called spongy bone. Spongy bone is softer than compact bone and contains many hollow spaces. Inside the shaft of long bones is the marrow, where blood cells are produced. Ligaments hold bones together at joints; cartilage provides cushioning that keeps the bones from rubbing against each other.

2. Students' answers might include the spine (gliding joints), shoulder (ball-and-socket joint), and elbow (hinge joint where the humerus meets the ulna, pivot joint where the humerus meets the radius).

Challenge Encourage students to investigate other kinds of joints found in the human skeleton, such as angular joints in the wrist and saddle joints in the thumb. How do the bones fit together in these joints? What movements do they permit?

Following Up

Baseline Assessment Return to the class drawings showing how students would look without bones. Have students supplement the sketches with a list of information learned in this investigation. Encourage them to recall the functions of the skeleton as they compile their lists.

Reteaching Discuss the investigation subconcept with students. Guide students to create a word web around the central term *skeleton*. You may wish to use the Activity Support Master "Word Web" (TRB p. 70).

Use *Science Notebook* p. 358.

◀ **Investigation Review**
Use Investigation Review p. 162 in the *Assessment Guide*.

How Do Bones and Muscles Cause Movement?

Planner

Subconcept Muscles contract and pull on bones, causing them to bend at joints and achieve movement; many injuries to bones and muscles can be avoided by taking precautions.

Objectives

- **Hypothesize** how muscles help bones to move.
- **Infer** how fatigue affects muscle performance.
- **Define** ways to avoid injury to bones and muscles.

Pacing 2–3 class periods

Science Terms skeletal muscles, smooth muscles, cardiac muscles, tendons, sprain, strain, fracture

Activate Prior Knowledge

Baseline Assessment Have students diagram how they think bones and muscles work together. Save their diagrams for use in Following Up.

Activity Push or Pull?

Preview *Students focus on the movement of their arms. They should hypothesize that bones move when pairs of muscles relax and contract; the contracting muscle pulls the bone, while the relaxing muscle permits the movement.*

1. Get Ready

Time about 30 minutes

Grouping pairs

Multi-Age Strategy Students who are adept at measuring can help their partners with the various arm measurements.

How Do Bones and Muscles Cause Movement?

Smack! You hit the ball far out into center field. You run as fast as you can—past first, past second, past third. Home run! Your skeletal system made it around the bases, but not without help from another system. Can you name it? It's your system of muscles!

Activity
Push or Pull?

MATERIALS
- tape measure
- *Science Notebook*

To make something move, you can either push it or pull it. Do your muscles push your bones to make them move, or pull them?

Procedure

1. The biceps is the muscle on the top of the upper arm. The triceps is the muscle on the bottom of the upper arm. Locate your biceps and triceps.

2. Wrap the fingers of your right hand around your left upper arm so you can feel both the top and bottom of your arm at the same time. Bend and straighten your forearm slowly several times. Describe in your *Science Notebook* how your biceps and triceps changed as you moved your arm.

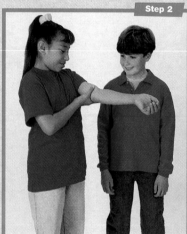

Step 2

G14

Responding to Individual Needs

Gifted and Talented Activity Students might enjoy investigating the muscle activities that cause different facial expressions. Encourage them to use anatomy books to identify the number of muscles involved in smiling, raising the eyebrows, and so on. They could also investigate how the muscles work together to cause the facial expression and if the facial structures are pushed or pulled.

3. Have a group member **measure** the length of your biceps and triceps when your arm is straight and when it is bent. **Make a chart** and **record** the measurements.

4. Have a group member **measure** the thickness around your arm when it is straight and when it is bent. Measure halfway between your elbow and shoulder. **Record** these measurements in your chart.

Analyze and Conclude

1. How did your biceps and triceps change as you bent and straightened your arm?

2. Based on your data, **hypothesize** how your muscles cause your bones to move. **Make a drawing** to show your hypothesis.

3. How do the biceps and triceps work together to cause your arm to move?

INVESTIGATE FURTHER!

EXPERIMENT

Add two rubber bands to the model you made for the activity on page G7. One rubber band should act like a biceps and one should act like a triceps. Compare your model with other students' models.

Step 3

Step 4

G15

Investigate Further

Experiment

Have students record their observations on p. 360 of their *Science Notebooks*. They should find that the biceps contracts when the model joint is flexed, while the triceps is relaxed. When the joint is straight, the triceps should be contracted while the biceps is relaxed.

Materials Hints Make sure students can understand the increments and scale listed on the tape measure.

Safety Review safety precautions with students.

2. Guide the Procedure

- To ensure that measurements are accurate, students can mark the point halfway between the elbow and shoulder with a fine-tipped washable marking pen to make a "landmark" site for all measurements.

- Students will have more accurate results if they roll up sleeves and measure against bare skin.

 Have students record their descriptions and measurements and answer questions on *Science Notebook* pp. 359–360.

 You might wish to have students use the CD-ROM Spreadsheet and Painter to organize and display their data.

3. Assess Performance

Process Skills Checklist

- Did students carefully **observe** the muscle changes caused by movement? Were their observations accurately **recorded**?

- Did students accurately **measure** the length of the biceps and triceps? Were the measurements accurately **recorded** in their charts?

- Did students **hypothesize** that flexing of the arm is caused by contraction of the biceps, which *pulls* the bone? Were the hypotheses based upon **observations** and **inferences**?

Analyze and Conclude

1. When the arm is straight, the triceps is contracted (larger) and the biceps is relaxed; as the arm flexes, the biceps contracts (becomes larger), while the triceps relaxes.

2. When one muscle contracts, the other relaxes. The contracted muscle pulls the bone, while the relaxed muscle permits this movement. Student drawings should show the relationship of the biceps and triceps, as shown on p. G18 of the student text.

3. Students should hypothesize that contraction of the biceps pulls the arm into a flexed position; relaxation of the triceps permits the movement.

Activity Tired Muscles

Preview *Students focus on repetitive use of a muscle group and should infer that as muscles fatigue, their ability to perform decreases.*

1. Get Ready

Time about 15 minutes

Grouping pairs

 Collaborative Strategy One student might record data as the other experiments with the clip. Students should then reverse roles.

Materials Hints Use small- to medium-sized spring clips so resistance to opening the clip repeatedly won't be too great for students.

Safety Review general safety precautions with students.

2. Guide the Procedure

- Make sure any student unable to open the clip participates by timing the activity and recording the data.

 Have students record data and answer questions on *Science Notebook* p. 361.

You may wish to have students use the CD-ROM Spreadsheet to organize and display their data.

3. Assess Performance

Process Skills Checklist
- Did students accurately **measure** and **record** the effects of repetitive activity on muscle performance?
- Did students **infer** that as muscles become fatigued, their ability to perform decreases?

Analyze and Conclude

1. Students should find that they were able to open the spring clip more times during the first trial than the second trial. Right-handed students should find that they were able to open the clip more times with their right hand, while left-handed students should find the reverse.

2. Students should infer that as muscles become fatigued, they become less able to open the clip.

3. Differences in right- and left-hand strength are related to the amount of use the muscles in the hand and arm receive. The dominant hand and arm are used for more frequent, repetitive activity; these muscles are better conditioned and fatigue less rapidly.

Activity
Tired Muscles

MATERIALS
- spring clip
- timer
- *Science Notebook*

Work can tire you out. What does feeling tired have to do with your muscles?

Procedure

1. While a group member watches the timer, count how many times you can open the spring clip with your right hand in 60 seconds. Record this number in your *Science Notebook* in a chart such as the one shown below.

2. Rest for one minute. Then repeat step 1.

3. Now repeat steps 1 and 2, using your left hand.

4. Compare your data with those of others.

Step 3

Name	Right Hand		Left Hand	
	Trial 1	Trial 2	Trial 1	Trial 2

Analyze and Conclude

1. Was there a difference in the number of times you opened the spring clip with your right hand between the first and second trial? Was there a difference with your left hand? Was there a difference in your performance between your right hand and your left hand?

2. Infer why any differences occurred.

3. Which muscles are stronger, those in your right hand and arm or those in your left hand and arm? Explain. Why do you think this must be so?

G16

 ## Responding to Individual Needs

Auditory Activity Encourage students to make up a verse or rhyme that describes the cause-and-effect relationship between muscle fatigue and decreased muscle performance. Allow students to recite their rhymes for the class. Or you may wish to have students display their poems on posters throughout the classroom.

How Do Muscles Work?

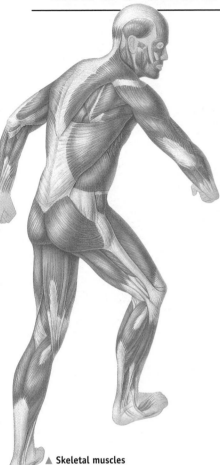

 When you think of muscles, you probably think of the fleshy bulges on your arms and legs. These muscles that are attached to bones are called **skeletal muscles**. The body also has two other kinds of muscles. The muscles of your digestive system—the ones that push food through the digestive organs—are called **smooth muscles**. The muscles of your heart that cause it to beat are called **cardiac muscles**.

Skeletal muscles are the kind that move your bones. Although they vary in size and shape, these muscles all have one thing in common: they are attached to bones by **tendons**, which are strong, ropelike fibers.

When you did the activity on pages G14 and G15, you discovered that the thickness of your biceps and triceps changed depending on whether you bent or straightened your arm. With

▲ Skeletal muscles   ▲ Smooth muscles   ▲ Cardiac muscles

G17

Integrating the Curriculum

Science & Language Arts

WRITING PLANS **What to Do** Tell students that proper muscle tone can be affected by activity choices. Have them develop and write an exercise plan to improve the muscular impairment of "rounded shoulders." Encourage students to use reference books to identify the muscles utilized in the exercise plans.

What's the Result? **What did your plan have to correct rounded shoulders?** Students should respond that the goal was to strengthen all muscles that support the shoulder, namely the trapezius and deltoid.

Why is it important to exercise both of the muscles that support the shoulder rather than just one or the other? Muscles work in pairs; if both muscles in a pair are strong, they work together smoothly.

How Do Muscles Work?

Preview *Students focus on the ways that muscles work together to cause the movement of bones.*

1. Get Ready

Science Terms skeletal muscles, smooth muscles, cardiac muscles, tendons

Background

- Skeletal muscles are called voluntary muscles because they are responsible for conscious movement, while smooth muscles and cardiac muscles are involuntary muscles because they are usually not under conscious control.

- As their name suggests, *skeletal muscles* are attached to bones; very simply, their function is to permit voluntary movements of the skeleton. Skeletal muscle cells can be one of two types: fast-twitch or slow-twitch. Fast-twitch muscles are used during activities that require speed and quick movements over a short period of time. Athletes such as sprinters, pole vaulters, and weight lifters generally have a high number of fast-twitch muscle cells. Long-distance athletes, such as runners, cyclists, and swimmers, generally have more of the slow-twitch muscle cells. These cells are used for activities that require endurance. The number of each type of cell a person has is an inherited trait and will not change with exercise.

Discussion Starter

When you clap your hands, what do you think happens in your arms? The arms bend at the elbows, moving forward from the shoulder in a path leading to a point in front of the body until the hands meet.

What makes this action possible? Bones and muscles work together to cause the arms to move. Students also might recognize that this action is voluntarily controlled.

2. Guide the Discussion

Choose from the following strategies to facilitate discussion.

Connecting to the Activities

- ***Push or Pull?, pp. G14–G15***

 What do you think would happen if both sets of muscles in your arm contracted at the same time? The bone would not move, because the muscles would be pulling in opposite directions.

Making Comparisons

- **How are tendons similar to ligaments?** Both tendons and ligaments are strong and ropelike. **How do they differ?** Ligaments hold bones together at joints; they allow some movement but generally keep the bones in place. Tendons connect skeletal muscles to bones.

Responding to Individual Needs

Students Acquiring English Encourage students to make a drawing of the attachment of the biceps and triceps to the bones of the arm. Help them label the muscles, bones, and tendons in English. Also help students describe the action that occurs at these junctures.

Visual/Spatial Activity To help students understand the relationship between bones and muscles, use **Transparency 33**, "Skeletal Muscles."

3. Assess Understanding

From your butcher, obtain a beef knee joint with muscles, ligaments, and tendons intact. Give students disposable plastic gloves to wear. Then let small groups of students examine and manipulate the joint. Encourage students to investigate which muscle pulls when the joint is flexed, the manner in which the tendons attach the muscles to the bones, and how the ligaments join the bones.

---

that data, you hypothesized about how your muscles cause your bones to move. Now check your hypothesis against an illustration of how the process works.

The drawings show how the two muscles work together. When the biceps contracts, the triceps stretches and relaxes, and the arm bends at the elbow. When the triceps contracts, the biceps stretches and relaxes, and the arm straightens. Movement of any part of your skeleton occurs when a pair of muscles alternately contract and relax. ■

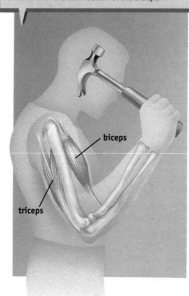
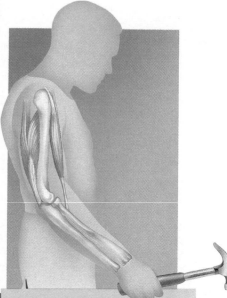

BICEPS CONTRACTED This person is ready to hit a nail with the hammer. The biceps is contracted, or shortened. It pulls on the bones of the forearm, and the arm bends at the elbow joint. The triceps on the opposite side of the upper arm is relaxed, or stretched. This allows the forearm to move with the contraction of the biceps.

biceps

triceps

TRICEPS CONTRACTED The person has hammered the nail hard. Notice the difference in the biceps and triceps. Now, the triceps is contracted, pulling the forearm down. The biceps is relaxed and stretched, which allows the triceps to move the forearm.

G18

Investigate Further

Integrating the Sciences

PHYSICAL SCIENCE

What to Do Tell students that muscle and joint movements cause bones to act as levers. Encourage them to use resource books to investigate levers and draw a diagram of a simple lever. Have students list instances in which the bones function as levers to move efficiently.

What's the Result? In the body, what are the levers? What are the fulcrums? Students should infer that bones are the levers, while joints serve as fulcrums. **How do muscles and joints cause bones to act as levers?** The bones are rods that can be moved about the fulcrum, or joint; muscles provide the force necessary for movement.

Multi-Age Classroom Provide reference books at varying levels of difficulty. Students can work in small groups to write lists.

Avoiding Bone and Muscle Injuries

You're dribbling down the court on a fast break. There's no one between you and the basket, and you can already see yourself making the winning points on an easy layup. This will be sweet. But then tragedy strikes. A terrible pain shoots through the back of your leg, and you stumble to the floor. As you grip your leg, you watch the ball—and your glory—roll out of bounds.

Of all the times to strain a muscle, this is the worst. Could you have prevented this injury? Maybe, if you had warmed up properly before the game.

Not all injuries to bones and muscles can be prevented. But if you use the proper equipment, exercise regularly, eat well, and get enough rest, you just may be able to make that winning basket or do something that would be equally as special to you.

Sprains, Strains, Tears, and Cramps

How are muscles and bones injured? One of the most common injuries to dancers and other athletes is the sprain. A **sprain** involves the tearing of a ligament at a joint. The ligament itself might tear, or the ligament might tear away from the bone. This usually happens when the joint is unnaturally

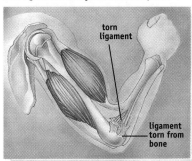

Torn ligaments at a joint cause a sprain. ▼

torn ligament

ligament torn from bone

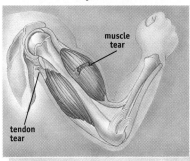

A strain results when a muscle or tendon is stretched too far or incurs a minor tear. A muscle tear is a major tear of a muscle. ▼

muscle tear

tendon tear

twisted because of a misstep or a blow. A sprain can be a slight injury or a serious injury that takes surgery to repair.

G19

Avoiding Bone and Muscle Injuries

Preview *Students focus on ways to prevent injuries to bones and muscle.*

1. Get Ready

Science Terms sprain, strain, fracture

Background

- Because few diagnostic tests exist to evaluate muscle, ligament, and tendon injuries, diagnosis is often made based on the appearance of the injured area. X-rays are most commonly used to diagnose bone injuries. MRI (magnetic resonance imaging) shows damage to bones as well as soft tissues, including muscles, tendons, and ligaments. Arthroscopy is a more invasive method of evaluating joint damage. In this procedure, a tiny scope is inserted into the joint so that the area can be directly viewed. Tiny surgical instruments can be passed through the scope, allowing the surgeon to correct any problem as soon as it is diagnosed. Arthroscopy enables surgeons to repair joint damage with far less trauma to the joint than traditional joint surgery; recovery time is greatly reduced, and rehabilitation can begin sooner.

- Fractures are generally classified as a complete fracture when a bone is broken into two or more pieces and an incomplete fracture when the break is not all the way across the bone. An open fracture is one in which the bone pierces the skin, while a closed fracture is one in which there is no break in the skin.

- Before beginning strenuous activity, one should do 5 to 10 minutes of mild warm-up exercises to limber up muscles. At the end of strenuous activity, one should do 5 to 10 minutes of cool-down exercises to slowly bring the body to a resting state.

Discussion Starter

- **What actions do people take to protect themselves from injury?** Answers might include staying away from hazardous situations, fastening seat belts, wearing motorcycle or bicycle helmets, and wearing protective sports equipment.

Cultural Connection

SURGERY REPORT **What to Do** Explain to students that Dr. Severo Ochoa, an American biochemist who won the Nobel Prize for synthesis of RNA, was also known for his study of energy sources used to contract muscles. Point out that research done by scientists such as Dr. Ochoa has led to new technology for treating injuries. While Aztec healers once used downy feathers, gum, resin, and rubber to set injured limbs, surgeons now use lasers to perform arthroscopic surgery. Suggest students find out more about arthroscopic surgery in encyclopedias and by calling the office of a local orthopedic surgeon or physical therapist. Have them write a report on their findings to share with the class.

What's the Result? What are the benefits of arthroscopy? It eliminates the need for large incisions and long recovery periods.

2. Guide the Discussion

Choose from the following strategies to facilitate discussion.

Making Comparisons

■ **How is your body like the mast of a sailboat?** In a sailboat, the mast is supported by a network of ropes and beams; in the body, the bones are held together and supported by a network of tendons and ligaments.

Drawing Conclusions

■ **If a rope were cut on a sailboat mast, what would happen?** The sail would not be able to be raised and lowered properly. **What would happen if tendons and ligaments were torn or injured?** The bones would not be supported, and joints would not be able to move properly.

Connecting to the Activities

• ***Push or Pull?, pp. G14–G15***
Draw students' attention to the model of a joint, with rubber bands added, that they made in the Investigate Further at the beginning of the investigation. Remind students that one rubber band represents the biceps, and while the other represents the triceps. **What happens to the biceps when the arm is flexed?** It contracts, or shortens. **What happens to the triceps when the arm is straightened?** It contracts. As students observe, remove one rubber band; demonstrate that the joint is no longer stable, and does not move in a coordinated manner.

A **strain**, in contrast, involves an overstretching or slight tearing of a muscle or a tendon that holds the muscle to the bone. A strain is sometimes called a "pulled muscle." If the muscle is stretched even farther, a muscle tear can result. A muscle tear takes weeks or months to heal.

Have you ever had a "charley horse"? A muscle contracts sharply and simply will not relax. This is called a muscle cramp. The cause of this is often muscle tiredness. Though painful for a moment, a muscle cramp usually does not result in serious injury.

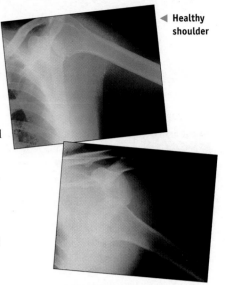
◄ Healthy shoulder

▲ In a dislocation, bones pull apart at a joint.

Fractures and Torn Cartilage

Bones are hard, but not so hard that they can't break. Luckily, since bones are living tissue, they almost always heal to become as good as new again.

Any break or crack of a bone is called a **fracture**. This term is used whether a bone is just slightly cracked or broken clear through. Unless the bone pierces the skin—which happens only in extreme cases—a fracture must be detected through an X-ray.

Torn cartilage, a tear in the padding at joints, often cannot be detected by X-rays. However, a technique called MRI does allow images of the cartilage to be filmed. The cartilage at joints does not heal as well as bones. For this reason, torn cartilage can be a lasting and troublesome injury.

How to Avoid Injuries

Accidents can happen to you, and sometimes you can't do anything to avoid them. But if you take precautions, you can usually avoid injury and disappointment.

First, wear the proper equipment when doing physical activities. You

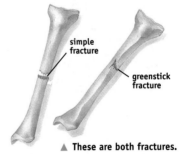
simple fracture

greenstick fracture

▲ These are both fractures.

G20

Integrating the Curriculum

 ### Science & Math

GRAPHING **What to Do** Discuss the importance of calcium in maintaining bone strength and muscle health. Have students research the calcium content in foods, including high- and low-fat dairy products, fish, and green vegetables. Encourage them to find the RDA of calcium for someone their age. Have students graph their findings, showing the milligrams of calcium found in a specified amount of each food. **What's the Result? Which foods were highest in calcium?** Examples might include low-fat dairy products, hard cheeses, sardines, canned salmon, and broccoli. **How could you get enough calcium to keep bones strong and muscles properly functioning?** Eat a variety of calcium-rich foods.

Suggest students use the CD-ROM Grapher to produce their graphs.

don't have to wear knee pads when playing soccer, but you'll avoid injuries if you do. And when you ride your bike or skate, wear a helmet. Can you think of other safety equipment that can help prevent injuries?

Second, do warm-up exercises before a physical activity and cool-down exercises when you're through. Your muscles need to stretch out a little before working hard. And they also need to stretch out after being used in a difficult dance or sport. Such stretching can help avoid strains and tears.

Avoid injuries by wearing a helmet, wrist guards, and elbow and knee pads while in-line skating. ▶

SCIENCE IN LITERATURE

PEAK PERFORMANCE
by Emily Isberg
Simon & Schuster, 1989

Kids are involved in competitive sports at younger and younger ages. But competition can lead to injuries to bones and muscles. By the age of 11, Siri Larsen had already been training as a gymnast for five years. Now she was representing Norway at international meets. But during one meet she misses the parallel bar and falls. X-rays show a fracture, a torn ligament, and a dislocation at the elbow.

In *Peak Performance* by Emily Isberg, you can read how sports medicine helped Siri make a remarkable comeback. You can also find out how football and basketball knee injuries occur—and what can be done to repair, and even prevent, them.

G21

Investigate Further

 ### Science, Technology & Society

What to Do The knee is the joint most vulnerable to injury. While it appears well protected by the synovial capsule (a protective fluid-filled sac), tendons, ligaments, and the kneecap, it is especially vulnerable to damage caused by sideways blows. These blows can tear both cartilage and ligaments. Have students learn how physical therapists treat ligament injuries of the knee. Ask students to investigate what exercises are used to rehabilitate knee injuries and what special equipment is used.

What's the Result? Students can display their findings on posterboard. Encourage them to diagram and illustrate the exercises needed to rehabilitate the various injuries.

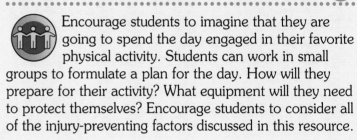
SCIENCE IN LITERATURE

*Peak Performance**
by Emily Isberg

Students can investigate what common injuries occur in sports such as basketball, tennis, and track. They might find out which similar injuries would require different types of rehabilitation for participation in different sports.

*Available in the Trade Book Library.

Responding to Individual Needs

Students Acquiring English Students can demonstrate the warm-up and cool-down exercises shown on p. G22, describing their actions both in their native languages and in English.

3. Assess Understanding

Encourage students to imagine that they are going to spend the day engaged in their favorite physical activity. Students can work in small groups to formulate a plan for the day. How will they prepare for their activity? What equipment will they need to protect themselves? Encourage students to consider all of the injury-preventing factors discussed in this resource.

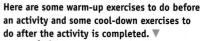

Close the Investigation

Critical Thinking Skills
Generating Ideas, Expressing Ideas, Solving Problems, Synthesizing

1. Movement of the leg occurs when a pair of muscles alternately contract and relax. First, one muscle contracts, flexing the knee and drawing back the bone in the lower leg; another muscle relaxes to permit this movement. Then the leg extends from the knee, moving forward until the foot contacts the ball; again, one muscle contracts while another relaxes.

2. Encourage students to consider posters, public-service announcements, and television commercials. Accept all reasonable efforts to devise a method to promote the use of bicycle helmets.

Challenge
Have students investigate the number of skull injuries resulting from bicycle accidents that your local emergency room treats annually. What age group is primarily affected? What long-term effects might remain after head injury? How is prognosis affected by the use of bicycle helmets?

Following Up

Baseline Assessment Return to students' diagrams of how bones and muscles work together to cause movement. Have them supplement their answers with material they learned in this investigation.

Reteaching To reinforce the concept that muscles pull bones to cause movement, help students contruct a simple lever. Tape a can to a flat surface and place a ruler on top of it. Use clay to secure a block to one end of the ruler. Push down on the other end. Help students to correlate the action of the lever to the movement of the bone and the force required to move the lever to the contraction of a muscle.

 Use *Science Notebook* p. 362.

Investigation Review ▶
Use Investigation Review p. 163 in the *Assessment Guide*.

Third, treat your body with respect. Eat the right foods—fruits and vegetables are the best. Also get enough sleep. A tired body is much more likely to be injured than a well-rested one. Stay away from alcohol and drugs. They can cause you to lose control.

What you do while you are young will affect you for the rest of your life. Now is the time for you to build the healthy body that will serve you well in the years ahead. ■

Here are some warm-up exercises to do before an activity and some cool-down exercises to do after the activity is completed. ▼

INVESTIGATION 2

1. Think about kicking a ball. Describe how the muscles and bones in your leg work together to cause this motion.

2. All studies show that wearing a helmet when riding a bicycle helps to prevent serious injuries and death. Still, many people ride without helmets. Think of a way to influence your classmates to always wear a helmet when they ride a bike.

Assessment

Investigation Review
How Do Bones and Muscles Cause Movement?

Name _____ Date _____

1. Use the words in the box to complete the sentences in the paragraph below.

arm	bend	biceps
relaxes	pairs	triceps

Skeletal muscles work in ___pairs___ to move parts of your body. The ___biceps___ and triceps in your arm work like a team. When the biceps contracts, the ___triceps___ muscle stretches and relaxes. These movements make your arm ___bend___ at the elbow. When the triceps contract, the other muscle of the pair ___relaxes___. That straightens your ___arm___.

2. Write the missing words.

kinds of muscle

a. ___Skeletal___ muscles move bones.

b. ___Smooth___ muscles are found in the stomach.

c. ___Cardiac___ muscles make up the heart.

muscle injuries

d. A ___cramp___ is a "charley horse."

e. A ___strain___ is an overstretched muscle.

f. A ___sprain___ is a torn ligament.

Answers may include wearing proper equipment such as a helmet and cycling shoes; doing warm-up exercises before a ride and cool-down exercises after a ride; eating healthy foods; and getting enough rest before and after a ride.

Process Skills
Communicating

Suppose you joined a bicycle club that will be riding long distances. What precautions can you take to prepare for these rides? What can you do to avoid injury? Write your answer on a separate sheet of paper.

Portfolio

Drawing Pictures Ask students to draw pictures to illustrate their two favorite ways of exercising. Encourage students to include bones, ligaments, tendons, and muscles in their drawings. They might indicate contraction and relaxation of the muscle pairs by showing several pictures in the correct sequence.

REFLECT & EVALUATE

WORD POWER

bone
cartilage
fracture
joint
strain
sprain

cardiac muscles
skeletal muscles
skeletal system
smooth muscles
ligaments
tendons

 **On Your Own**
Review the terms in the list. Then make two lists to show those terms that relate to bones and those that relate to muscles.

 With a Partner
Write each term in the list on one side of an index card and the definition on the other side. Use the cards to quiz your partner.

BUILD YOUR PORTFOLIO

Draw a diagram of the skeletal muscles, such as the one on page G17. Use an encyclopedia or library book to label some of the major muscles.

Analyze Information

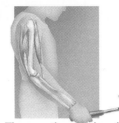

Study the drawings. Then use them to describe, in your own words, how the biceps and triceps work together to cause the forearm to move.

Assess Performance

Design a test to determine whether the muscles in your right upper leg or your left upper leg are stronger. After your teacher has reviewed your design, work with a partner to carry out the test. Compare your results with those of others.

Problem Solving

1. Compare your skeleton, which is on the inside of the body, to the skeleton of an insect, which is on the outside of the body. What are some advantages and disadvantages of each?

2. For a moment, pretend that the gliding joints in your ankles are replaced with hinge joints. What changes would this cause in how you are able to move?

3. Imagine that you're the trainer for a famous ballet dancer. What things would you suggest to avoid bone and muscle injuries?

G23

REFLECT & EVALUATE

Word Power

 On Your Own Students' use of the terms should reflect an understanding of their meanings.

 With a Partner Students should use the Glossary to check definitions.

Analyze Information

When the biceps contracts, the triceps stretches and relaxes, and the arm bends at the elbow. When the triceps contracts, the biceps stretches and relaxes, and the arm straightens out.

Assess Performance

One test would be to cross one leg over the other, suspend a kilogram from the dangling foot, and count how many times the person can swing the weighted leg back and forth in one or two minutes.

Problem Solving

1. A possible advantage is that skin and muscles would be protected from cuts and scrapes. Possible disadvantages include that the body would lose its flexibility and speed.

2. The foot would be limited to the types of motion the leg has at the knee.

3. Suggestions include wearing proper equipment that fits correctly. The trainer would make sure that the dancer did warm-up and cool-down exercises, ate a healthful diet, was well-rested, and abstained from alcohol and illegal drugs.

 Use *Science Notebook* pp. 363–364.

BUILD YOUR PORTFOLIO

Check that students' diagrams are reasonably drawn and correctly labeled.

 Suggest that students use the CD-ROM Writer and Painter to make and label their diagrams.

Chapter Test   pp. 164–165 in the Assessment Guide

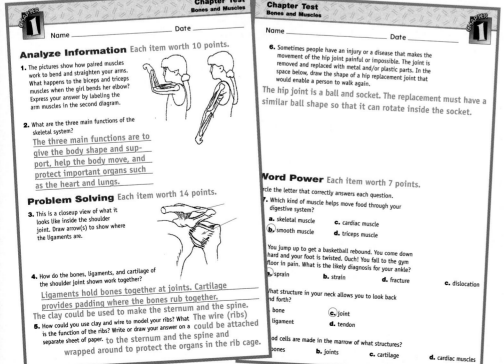

Chapter Test
Bones and Muscles

Name _____ Date _____

Analyze Information Each item worth 10 points.

1. The pictures show how paired muscles work to bend and straighten your arms. What happens to the biceps and triceps muscles when the girl bends her elbow? Express your answer by labeling the arm muscles in the second diagram.

2. What are the three main functions of the skeletal system?
The three main functions are to give the body shape and support, help the body move, and protect important organs such as the heart and lungs.

Problem Solving Each item worth 14 points.

3. This is a closeup view of what it looks like inside the shoulder joint. Draw arrow(s) to show where the ligaments are.

4. How do the bones, ligaments, and cartilage of the shoulder joint shown work together?
Ligaments hold bones together at joints. Cartilage provides padding where the bones rub together.

5. How could you use clay and wire to model your ribs? What is the function of the ribs? Write or draw your answer on a separate sheet of paper.
The clay could be used to make the sternum and the spine. The wire (ribs) could be attached to the sternum and the spine and wrapped around to protect the organs in the rib cage.

Chapter Test
Bones and Muscles

Name _____ Date _____

6. Sometimes people have an injury or a disease that makes the movement of the hip joint painful or impossible. The joint is removed and replaced with metal and/or plastic parts. In the space below, draw the shape of a hip replacement joint that would enable a person to walk again.
The hip joint is a ball and socket. The replacement must have a similar ball shape so that it can rotate inside the socket.

Word Power Each item worth 7 points.
Circle the letter that correctly answers each question.

7. Which kind of muscle helps move food through your digestive system?
a. skeletal muscle
b. smooth muscle
c. cardiac muscle
d. triceps muscle

You jump up to get a basketball rebound. You come down hard and your foot is twisted. Ouch! You fall to the gym floor in pain. What is the likely diagnosis for your ankle?
a. sprain
b. strain
c. dislocation
d. fracture

What structure in your neck allows you to look back and forth?
a. bone
b. ligament
c. joint
d. tendon

Blood cells are made in the marrow of what structures?
a. bones
b. joints
c. cartilage
d. cardiac muscles

CHAPTER 2 — THE NERVOUS SYSTEM

Subconcepts	Activities	Materials
Investigation 1 What Role Do the Brain and Nerves Play?		

The brain is the control center of the nervous system; neurons carry messages between the brain and all other parts of the body.
 	
Suggested Pacing: 2–3 class periods
Standards
  pp. 156, 157
Benchmarks
  pp. 136, 140
	Walk Straight and Tall, p. G26
	Science Processes: observe, communicate, infer, predict
	
	Measuring Reaction Time, p. G27
	Science Processes: observe; measure; communicate; infer; predict; collect, record, and interpret data; identify and control variables
		book, *Science Notebook* p. 367
		
		meterstick*, *Science Notebook* p. 368

Investigation 2 How Can You Respond to Things Around You?		

The sense receptors collect information from the environment for the brain to interpret and respond to; reflexes allow the nervous system to respond to danger automatically.
 	
Suggested Pacing: 4–5 class periods
Standards
  pp. 156, 157
Benchmarks
  pp. 132, 136, 140, 141
	Test Your Mind, p. G34
	Science Processes: measure; communicate; infer; predict; collect, record, and interpret data; identify and control variables; experiment
	
	Reflex Action, p. G36
	Science Processes: observe; communicate; infer; predict; collect, record, and interpret data
		index cards*, marker*, timer*, Activity Support Masters G2–G3 (TRB pp. 65–66), *Science Notebook* p. 371
		
		chair, *Science Notebook* pp. 373–374

Overview

In this chapter students investigate how the brain and nerves work together as the nervous system. They learn about reflexes, the five senses, and the power of the mind.

Chapter Concept

The nervous system—including the brain, spinal cord, nerves, and sense organs—takes in information from the environment, stores memories, controls actions, and directs the body's response.

Advance Preparation	Curriculum Connection	Assessment
Walk Straight and Tall None **Measuring Reaction Time** None	Math TG p. G28 Cultural Connection TG p. G29 The Arts TG p. G30 Integrating the Sciences TG p. G31 Literature TG p. G32	**Chapter 2 Baseline Assessment:** *Science Notebook* pp. 365–366 **Investigation 1 Baseline Assessment:** TG p. G26 **Investigation 1 Review:** AG p. 166 **Think It/Write It,** p. G33; *Science Notebook* p. 370 **Following Up on Baseline Assessment:** TG p. G33 **Portfolio:** TG p. G33
Test Your Mind None **Reflex Action** None	Integrating the Sciences TG p. G37 Cultural Connection TG p. G38, G40 Social Studies TG p. G39 Language Arts TG p. G42 Science, Technology, & Society TG p. G43	**Investigation 2 Baseline Assessment:** TG p. G34 **Investigation 2 Review:** AG p. 167 **Think It/Write It,** p. G44; *Science Notebook* p. 376 **Following Up on Baseline Assessment:** TG p. G44 **Performance:** TG p. G44 **Chapter 2 Summative Assessment** Reflect and Evaluate, p. G45 Chapter 2 Review/Test: AG pp. 168–169 *Science Notebook* pp. 377–378

TG= Teaching Guide   TRB= Teacher Resource Book   AG= Assessment Guide   *Materials in Equipment Kit

Chapter Overview

Chapter Concept The nervous system—including the brain, spinal cord, nerves, and sense organs—takes in information from the environment, stores memories, controls actions, and directs the body's responses.

Theme: Systems

Interactions between the nervous system and the other body systems are evidence of the control exercised by the nervous system.

Common Misconceptions

Although students relate thinking, learning, and memory to the brain, they may still infer metaphysical explanations of these activities, rather than ascribing them to brain structures and processes.

Options for
Setting the Stage

Warm-Up Activity

 Have students work in pairs, and have one partner lightly place a blindfolded partner's hand on different surfaces in succession. When the blindfolded partner cannot guess the surface, it will become apparent that the brain needs more information to identify the object.

 Use *Science Notebook* pp. 365–366.

Discussion Starter:
Snails on the Scent

Use the photo and text to start a discussion about senses.

- **Why do you think some neurobiologists study a snail's sense of smell and taste instead of the nervous system of humans?** It is easier to study the snail's less complex brain. What is learned can often be applied to humans.

- **Career:** *Neurobiologist*
Tell students that a neurobiologist is a scientist who studies the anatomy, physiology, and pathology of the nervous system. Neurobiologists involved in research hope to someday explain how "thinking" occurs in the brain.

CHAPTER 2

THE NERVOUS SYSTEM

Have you ever been nervous? Your hands tremble, your stomach muscles tighten, and your mouth gets dry. Your nervous system senses things about your surroundings and causes your body to respond. How does the nervous system control and coordinate what your body does?

Snails on the Scent

What can you smell? Burning leaves? Sour milk? Chocolate cake? You may think you have a keen sense of smell. But among the creatures of the animal kingdom, humans have a rather dull sense of smell.

Ronald Chase is a neurobiologist (nōo′rō bī äl′ə jist), a scientist who studies the nervous system. At McGill University in Montreal, Canada, he has investigated the land snail's sense of smell. Land snails have been around for about 350 million years. Half of the brain of a land snail deals mainly with smells and tastes.

Dr. Chase has spent years training snails to follow different smells by rewarding them with food. He has even taught snails to follow smells they don't like! Chase claims to have set a record by training snails to remember particular scents for as long as 120 days.

Do you think humans' sense of smell would improve if it were the only way to find food?

G24

Home-School Connection

 The Explore at Home activity "The Brain Game" encourages students to observe how the human brain learns and remembers. Distribute the activity (TRB p. 35) when students have completed the chapter. Ask students to tell how successfully the members of their families played the game.

Explore at Home

Name _____   Date _____

THE BRAIN GAME

If you have a pack of playing cards, you and family members can play a game to discover together how the human brain learns and remembers.

Materials

✓ deck of playing cards
✓ stop watch or clock with second hand

Procedure

Gather together family members around a table. Select eight pairs of playing cards from the deck, matching by numbers rather than by suits. Mix up the cards and lay them on the table, number-side down, in four rows of four. Select one family member to begin turning over cards until matches are made. Time this player and record the results in the Data Table. Then turn all the cards number-side down again

in the same locations and have the same family member try again. Time and record the results. Follow the same procedures for other family members, mixing up the cards each time a new player begins. You might like to play again by selecting matching suits, rather than numbers.

Results

Did different family members take different amounts of time to do the initial matches? What happened on their second try? Talk with your family about how learning takes place in the cerebrum and about how all of you have different learning times.

Data Table

Family member	First try	Second try

INVESTIGATION 1

WHAT ROLE DO THE BRAIN AND NERVES PLAY?
.... G26

INVESTIGATION 2

HOW CAN YOU RESPOND TO THINGS AROUND YOU?
.... G34

◄ Dr. Ronald Chase tests the land snail's sense of smell.

Technology Alert

Videodisc

Emergency Segment 2

In segment 2 of the videodisc entitled *Emergency*, students learn about adrenaline, a hormone released by the adrenal glands during emergencies. Adrenaline causes a person's breathing and heartbeat rate to increase by sending more blood to the brain and certain muscles while reducing the blood flow to other parts of the body. This response of the endocrine system is automatic, that is, the glands release the hormone without the person having to think about it.

Chapter Road Map

INVESTIGATION 1

What Role Do the Brain and Nerves Play?

Activities	**Resources**
✳ Walk Straight and Tall	✳ The Path of a Nerve Impulse
✳ Measuring Reaction Time	✳ A Tour of the Brain

INVESTIGATION 2

How Can You Respond to Things Around You?

Activities	**Resources**
Test Your Mind	✳ The Senses
✳ Reflex Action	Stages of Mental Development
	✳ The Path of a Reflex
	Brain Power

*Pressed for Time?

As you work through the upcoming investigations, focus on the activities and resources identified by the clock.

🔷 Look for this symbol in front of questions that help develop Scientific Reasoning Skills.

WHAT ROLE DO THE BRAIN AND NERVES PLAY?

Planner

Subconcept The brain is the control center of the nervous system; neurons carry messages between the brain and all other parts of the body.

Objectives

- **Observe** how the body responds to stimuli.
- **Identify** the functions of the parts of the brain.
- **Describe** how nerve impulses travel.

Pacing 2–3 class periods

Science Terms nerve impulse, neurons, sensory neurons, stimuli, motor neurons, cerebrum, cerebellum, medulla

Activate Prior Knowledge

Baseline Assessment Throw a foam ball to a student. Ask students to describe the reactions. Save responses for Following Up.

INVESTIGATION 1

WHAT ROLE DO THE BRAIN AND NERVES PLAY?

Think about the operation of a clothing-store chain. Workers in each store call Headquarters with reports on what's selling. Headquarters makes decisions and calls back, saying, "Put slacks on sale; order more shirts!" Now investigate what goes on in your body's "head-quarters" and how messages get there and back.

Activity

Walk Straight and Tall

How do muscles and bones work together with the brain and nerves? This activity will help you understand how.

MATERIALS
- book
- *Science Notebook*

Procedure

Try to balance a book on your head and walk across the room without dropping it. Before you do this, **predict** what you think will happen. **Record** your prediction in your *Science Notebook*. Have a partner **observe** you as you walk while balancing the book. Each of you **record** your own observations. Next, **observe** as your partner walks across the room. Again, each **record** your own observations.

Analyze and Conclude

1. How did your observations compare to your prediction?

2. How did muscles and bones enable you to balance a book on your head and to walk across the room? **Infer** what role your nervous system played in this activity.

G26

Activity Walk Straight and Tall

Preview *Students walk while balancing a book on their head and focus on how they accomplish the task.*

1. Get Ready

Time about 15 minutes

Grouping pairs

Multi-Age Strategy Students of different ages will have varying success at balancing the book. Point out that the activity is about what your body does to keep balance.

2. Guide the Procedure

What did you have to do to keep the book balanced? Were you surprised? Students may be surprised at the slight motions they had to make to balance the books.

 Have students record their predictions and observations, and answer questions on *Science Notebook* p. 367.

 Students could use the CD-ROM Painter to display their observations.

3. Assess Performance

Process Skills Checklist

- Did students **predict** how they would balance the book?
- Did students **observe** how different parts of the body moved to keep the book balanced?
- Did students **infer** that the brain directed information?

Analyze and Conclude

1. Observations should coincide with predictions.
2. The nervous system analyzed information and sent messages for muscles and bones to work together.

Activity

Measuring Reaction Time

How are your brain and nerves needed for you to react to a falling object? How long does it take them to "get the message"?

MATERIALS
• meterstick
• *Science Notebook*

Step 2

Procedure

1. Hold out your arm and spread your thumb and forefinger slightly apart.

2. Have your partner hold a meterstick above your hand so that the 0-cm end of the stick is between your thumb and finger.

3. Without warning, your partner will let go of the meterstick. **Predict** at which centimeter mark you will catch the falling meterstick. **Record** your prediction in your *Science Notebook*.

4. Catch the meterstick as it falls. Look at the centimeter mark where you caught it. **Record** that number in a chart.

5. Repeat steps 1 through 4 nine more times. **Compare** your data with that of other groups.

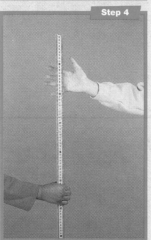

Step 4

Analyze and Conclude

1. The time it takes the body to recognize and react to something is called reaction time. How did your reaction time change as you did this activity? Why do you think it changed?

2. What do you think happens between your eyes, brain, and hand from the time the meterstick starts to fall until you catch it?

3. **Infer** why there was a reaction time between when you saw the meterstick fall and when you caught it.

G27

Responding to Individual Needs

Logical/Mathematical Activity Students can graph their improvement over the ten times they caught the meterstick. Ask them to explain the pattern of improvement they see. You may wish to have students use the CD-ROM Grapher or Activity Support Master "Graph Paper" (TRB p. 67) for their graphs. **Does this graph have enough information to tell if you could keep reducing your reaction time? Explain.** Students may suggest that they could reduce reaction time further, but there would be a point at which it could not be further reduced.

Activity — Measuring Reaction Time

Preview *Students test their reaction times by catching a falling meterstick and should find that their times improve with practice.*

1. Get Ready

Time about 20 minutes

Grouping pairs

Multi-Age Strategy Students should take turns dropping the meterstick, making predictions, and recording each other's observations.

Safety Check that metersticks have no rough or sharp edges.

2. Guide the Procedure

• Remind students to hold the meterstick at the same place each time, with the 0-cm mark aligned with the top edge of the catcher's hand.

• **Why is it important to start off each trial with the meterstick in the same place?** This allows the results of each trial to be compared.

• **Where should you take the measurement?** From top of fingers or fist that grasps the meterstick

• Encourage students to compare their predictions with their results. Were their reaction times longer than they predicted?

Students may record their predictions, measurements, and answers to questions on *Science Notebook* p. 368.

You may have students use the CD-ROM Spreadsheet to organize and display their data.

3. Assess Performance

Process Skills Checklist

• Did students **predict** how fast they thought they could catch the meterstick?

• Did students use the same method to **measure** accurately each time?

• Did students **record** their data after each trial?

Analyze and Conclude

1. The reaction time probably shortened slightly as the brain learned what to anticipate.

2. The eyes see the falling stick. The brain receives that message and sends a message to the hand.

3. There was a reaction time because the messages sent take time to travel.

The Path of a
Nerve Impulse

Preview *Students focus on the role of neurons in transmitting messages between the brain and other parts of the body.*

1. Get Ready

Science Terms nerve impulse, neurons, sensory neurons, stimuli, motor neurons

Background

- The short extensions of a nerve cell are called dendrites. The long extension of a nerve cell is called an axon. Some axons are only a few thousandths of an inch long; others extend the length of the leg, from the spinal cord in the back to the tip of a toe.

- The space between nerve cells is the synapse. When an electrical impulse, or message, reaches the tip of an axon, a chemical is released into the synapse. When the chemical reaches the dendrites of the next nerve cell, an impulse is initiated and continues through that cell. Neural impulses travel this way from one nerve cell to another.

Discussion Starter

The nervous system sends and receives messages to and from the brain. What do you think the parts of the nervous system might be? Brain, spinal cord, and nerves **Where in the nervous system do you think nerves might be located?** Students might infer that nerves carry messages from locations throughout the body.

2. Guide the Discussion

Choose from the following strategies to facilitate discussion.

Thinking Critically

- **What are some stimuli in the environment that might start a nerve impulse?** Any phenomenon that can be sensed could serve as a stimulus. Students might mention sights, sounds, smells, tastes, and touches.

The Path of a
Nerve Impulse

Do you think you responded quickly to the falling meterstick in the activity on page G27? No matter how fast you grabbed the meterstick, there was still a little time that passed after you saw it fall. This time—your reaction time—was the time it took for a nerve impulse to make its way through your nervous system.

A **nerve impulse** is a message carried through your body by nerve cells, or **neurons** (noo′ränz). Neurons are found throughout your body.

Certain neurons, the **sensory neurons**, pick up signals from the environment. These signals, or **stimuli** (stim′yoo li), start a nerve impulse. Your muscles move in reaction to the messages carried to them by another type of neuron, the **motor neurons.** Bundles of neurons are called nerves.

What happens between a stimulus and your response? To answer this question, follow the path of the nerve impulse in the illustration on page G29.

Now you know the path of a nerve impulse. These impulses are similar to electrical signals and are caused by changes in chemicals in the neurons. A nerve impulse can travel through your nervous system at speeds from 10 to 120 m/s. That's why you can respond so quickly to a stimulus. ■

In a neuron, impulses travel along extensions to other neurons. ▼

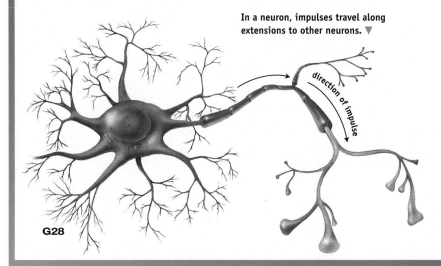

direction of impulse

G28

Integrating the Curriculum

Science & Math

MAKING GRAPHS **What to Do** Have each pair of students write on the chalkboard their meterstick measurements for the activity. Students can then work in the same pairs to graph the data of the whole class. You might suggest that students prepare their graphs with the CD-ROM Grapher.

What's the Result? **What does this graph show?** The graph will likely show a range of measurements, which translates into a range of reaction times among students. The graph might be a bell curve, with most students' reaction times falling in the middle range.

Multi-Age Classroom Make sure both students of each pair have a chance to record data for the whole class.

FOLLOWING THE NERVE IMPULSE

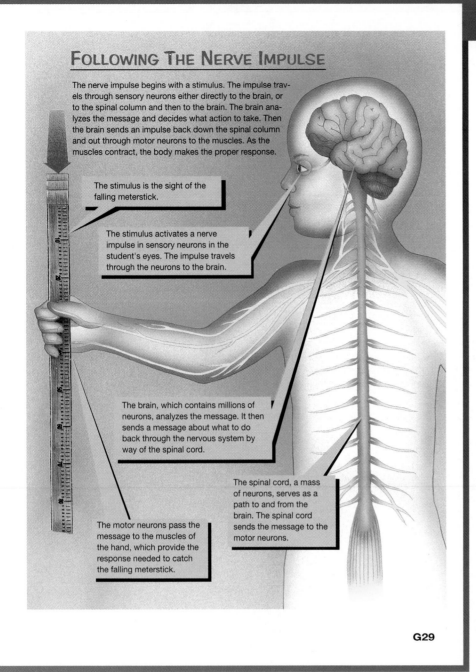

The nerve impulse begins with a stimulus. The impulse travels through sensory neurons either directly to the brain, or to the spinal column and then to the brain. The brain analyzes the message and decides what action to take. Then the brain sends an impulse back down the spinal column and out through motor neurons to the muscles. As the muscles contract, the body makes the proper response.

The stimulus is the sight of the falling meterstick.

The stimulus activates a nerve impulse in sensory neurons in the student's eyes. The impulse travels through the neurons to the brain.

The brain, which contains millions of neurons, analyzes the message. It then sends a message about what to do back through the nervous system by way of the spinal cord.

The spinal cord, a mass of neurons, serves as a path to and from the brain. The spinal cord sends the message to the motor neurons.

The motor neurons pass the message to the muscles of the hand, which provide the response needed to catch the falling meterstick.

G29

Investigate Further

Cultural Connection

What to Do Tell students that acupuncture is a medical therapy that originated in ancient China. Acupuncture involves inserting thin needles into parts of the surface of the body. Scientists think that acupuncture works through the nervous system by blocking messages of pain sent by nerves. Have interested students research acupuncture and prepare a report on their findings.

What's the Result? Let students share their reports with the class. Hold a follow-up discussion in which students cite reasons for using acupuncture.

Multi-Age Classroom Students could work in small groups to research facts for their reports.

Connecting to the Activities

- *Walk Straight and Tall*, p. G26

Describe step by step the work of neurons in a person who is trying to walk while balancing a book on his or her head. The stimulus (the feel of the book on the head) activates nerve impulses that travel to the brain. The brain analyzes the messages and sends messages via the spinal cord about how the body should shift to continue balancing the book.

Drawing Conclusions

- **The short extensions of a neuron are called dendrites, from the Greek word *dendron*. Look at the illustration on page G28. What do you think *dendron* means?** *Dendron* means "tree." Students should see the analogy between this word and the treelike branching of dendrites.

Identifying and Solving Problems

Suppose part of a person's spinal cord was damaged. How might this condition affect that person? Damage to the spinal cord could affect a person's abilities to move parts of his or her body. Messages may not be able to get to a person's legs, for example. The legs would be unable to move even though nothing is wrong with the legs themselves.

Responding to Individual Needs

Students Acquiring English Visually demonstrate the path of a nerve impulse. Draw a few neurons on the chalkboard. The neurons should be end-to-end with a little space between them. Use different colors of chalk to trace the path of an impulse as it passes through a neuron, crosses the space between neurons, and continues through the next neuron.

Visual/Spatial Activity Use **Transparency 35**, "Following the Nerve Impulse," to help students trace the pathway of an impulse.

3. Assess Understanding

 Have students describe the difference between a sensory neuron and a motor neuron. Ask: **Why do we need both kinds?** A sensory neuron carries messages from the source of the stimulus to the brain; the motor neuron carries messages from the brain to muscles and other parts of the body. Both are needed to respond to stimuli. Activity Support Master "Compare-Contrast Diagram" (TRB p. 68) may help students organize their information.

RESOURCE

A Tour of the Brain

Preview *Students focus on functions of the three main parts of the brain.*

1. Get Ready

Science Terms cerebrum, cerebellum, medulla

Background

- The connecting band of neurons that joins the two hemispheres of the cerebrum is called the corpus callosum. The corpus callosum allows the cerebral hemispheres to communicate with each other.

- The brain does not contain any nerve endings sensitive to pain. Therefore, brain surgery can be performed on a conscious patient. Part of the skull can be removed under local anesthesia, exposing the brain for surgery. Gray and white matter can be cut or cauterized without the patient experiencing pain.

- All nerve impulses that are sent to the brain are electrochemically the same. The area of the brain that receives the messages determines how they are interpreted. If messages from the ears were sent to the seeing part of the brain, sounds would be interpreted as images.

Discussion Starter

- **What does your brain allow you to do?** Students may name thinking, feeling, directing the movement of their muscles and limbs, and directing the activities of their major organs.

A Tour of the Brain

"All aboard for a tour of the brain! Check all sharp objects at the gate. Once we get past the skull, we must ensure that the soft tissue of the brain remains uninjured by our journey. Take your seats, please. Here we go!"

Off to a Bony Start

What if you could take a tour of the brain? You'd have to shrink yourself down to board a miniature inner-space ship that will make its way through the complex structure of this control center of the nervous system.

Your first obstacle will be getting through the brain's protective covering, the skull. The brain is composed of very soft tissue. Without the skull the brain could be seriously injured by the slightest bump. In addition to the bony covering, the brain is protected by three layers of membranes, one of which is tough and leathery. Finally, a watery fluid surrounds the brain, cushioning it from any impact.

Once inside, you'll find an extremely complex organ containing about 15 billion neurons—not surprising, considering the important role the brain plays in the body! You'll see that the brain has three main parts: the cerebrum, the cerebellum, and the medulla.

The three main parts of the brain together weigh about 1.5 kg (3 lb). ▼

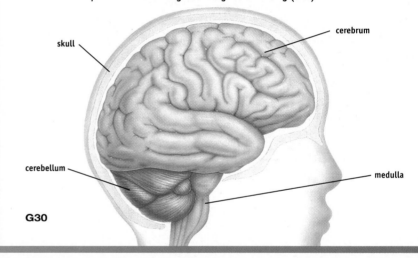

G30

Integrating the Curriculum

Science & the Arts

BRAIN MODELS

What to Do Have groups of students make models of the human brain using different colors of modeling clay to designate the three sections. Small flags made of toothpicks and paper can be used to label body parts controlled by the different areas of the cerebrum.

What's the Result? **Which part of the brain takes up most of the space inside the skull?** The cerebrum **Which part connects the spinal cord with the brain's center?** The medulla **How is the cerebellum's shape like that of the cerebrum?** Both have two halves.

Multi-Age Classroom Group members could discuss and agree on procedures to follow when making their brain model.

Rolling Gray Hills and Valleys

Once inside the skull, you'll find yourself in the **cerebrum** (sə rē′ brəm), the largest part of the brain. You can easily get lost in the cerebrum, since its outer layer—the cortex—contains many folds and grooves. These folds give the brain an increased surface area—more thinking space. Your first impression will be one of total grayness. The outer part of the cerebrum contains the gray matter of the brain.

The cerebrum is divided into two halves, or hemispheres. A band of neurons connects the halves, carrying nerve impulses from one to the other.

Thinking takes place in your cerebrum. It is where you store memories and make decisions. The cerebrum is also the place where your emotions and attitudes originate. Notice on the map the cerebral areas controlling different parts of the body.

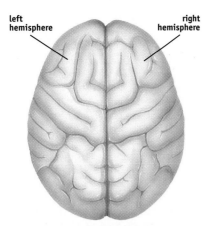

left hemisphere   right hemisphere

▲ In general, the right half of the cerebrum controls the left side of the body, and the left half controls the right side.

Body parts and functions controlled by areas of the cerebrum ▼

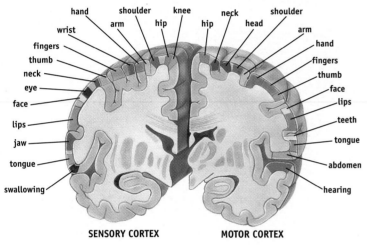

hand   shoulder   knee   neck   shoulder
wrist   arm   hip   hip   head   arm
fingers   hand
thumb   fingers
neck   thumb
eye   face
face   lips
lips   teeth
jaw   tongue
tongue   abdomen
swallowing   hearing

SENSORY CORTEX   MOTOR CORTEX

G31

Investigate Further

Integrating the Sciences

EARTH SCIENCE

What to Do Scientists who study human fossils take careful measurements of skulls and study skull parts. Students could diagram skull sizes of human ancestors, showing relative brain capacity. They could begin with *Australopithecus afarensis*.

What's the Result? Students may display their diagrams and hypothesize about the relationship between increase in brain size among ancestral species and the development of more complex behavior and culture.

Multi-Age Classroom Students who are adept at diagraming could assist others with their skull diagrams.

2. Guide the Discussion

Choose from the following strategies to facilitate discussion.

Thinking Critically

- Measure the area of a soft towel. Then bunch up the cloth so that it is a wrinkled ball. **Has the surface area of the towel changed?** No **What is the advantage of the cerebrum's having many folds like this towel?** The folds allow a large surface area to fit inside a relatively small cavity.

Making Inferences

 A stroke occurs when the blood supply to the brain is impaired. Suppose a person who has had a stroke has trouble moving the left arm and leg. What can you say about the part of the brain that has been damaged? Students should infer that since the right side of the cerebrum controls motor movement on the left side of the body, the person had damage to the right side of the cerebrum.

Responding to Individual Needs

Students Acquiring English Referring to the diagram of the brain on the bottom of p. G31, have students say in English the different body parts controlled by different areas of the cerebrum.

Visual/Spatial Activity Help students understand the structure of the brain by using **Transparency 34**, "Parts of the Brain."

Connecting to the Activities

- **Measuring Reaction Time, p. G27**
  Tell students to look at the drawing on p. G33. Direct them to trace with their fingers the path of the nerve impulses that were generated when they tried to catch the measuring stick during the activity.

Making Inferences

- **You're standing at the free-throw line with the basketball in your hands. How are you using the different parts of your brain as you shoot the free throw?** Your cerebrum makes you aware of the environment (eg., the location of the basket) and has the memory of how to throw the ball. Your cerebellum coordinates the movements of your hands and arms so that you can carry out the actions that you know how to do. The medulla directs your breathing, heart rate, and other life functions that have to be performed for you to be shooting the free throw in the first place.

SCIENCE IN LITERATURE

Peak Performance
by Emily Isberg

Students could draw a diagram showing how the "visualizing" technique they read about in this book might affect various parts of an athlete's body.

Responding to Individual Needs

Gifted and Talented Activity Students could use reference books to find out about disorders of the brain and the nervous system. Ask students to describe each disorder, which part of the brain is affected, and how each disorder affects the person who is afflicted with it. Students may support their findings with diagrams, if appropriate.

3. Assess Understanding

Working in groups of three, students can pretend each of them is one of the three different parts of the brain. Give each group five minutes to develop a master list of as many functions of their part of the brain as they can think of and then act out these functions. Encourage students to go beyond the examples named in the book if they can.

South of the Cerebrum

After exploring the gray matter, you'll go to the cerebellum, below and to the rear of the cerebrum. The **cerebellum** (ser ə bel'əm), the second largest part of the brain, coordinates the body's muscles. Your sense of balance comes from the cerebellum.

When you first learn a physical activity—a dance routine or swim stroke—you are really training the cerebellum. The nerve impulses that direct your muscles start in the cerebrum but pass through the cerebellum on their way to your muscles. The cerebellum makes sure your movements are smooth and coordinated.

Last Stop

No trip to the brain would be complete without a stop at the medulla. The **medulla** (mi dul'ə) connects the brain to the spinal column. You'll probably notice that, in addition to some gray neuron groups, the medulla contains white matter.

The medulla controls the involuntary actions of the body—the actions that you don't think about. These include heart rate, blood pressure, breathing, blinking, and coughing. Imagine if you had to think about all those actions all the time! The medulla directs such basic functions, leaving your cerebrum free to take care of other things.

SCIENCE IN LITERATURE

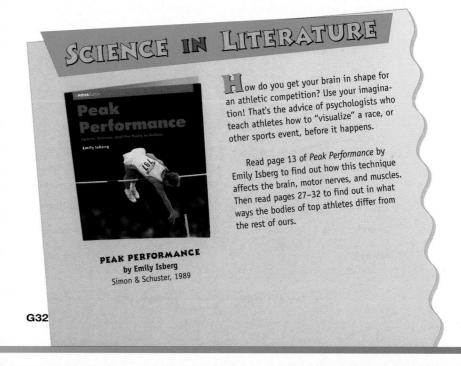

How do you get your brain in shape for an athletic competition? Use your imagination! That's the advice of psychologists who teach athletes how to "visualize" a race, or other sports event, before it happens.

Read page 13 of *Peak Performance* by Emily Isberg to find out how this technique affects the brain, motor nerves, and muscles. Then read pages 27–32 to find out in what ways the bodies of top athletes differ from the rest of ours.

PEAK PERFORMANCE
by Emily Isberg
Simon & Schuster, 1989

G32

Investigate Further

Take Action

Students may find that head injuries can result in concussion, which occurs when a blow to the head causes temporary brain dysfunctions. Symptoms may include loss of consciousness, headaches, or temporary memory lapses. Other types of brain injuries, such as strokes, accidents, or brain tumors, may result in paralysis. Wearing helmets during physical activities such as cycling, skating, or contact sports will help prevent head injuries. Students should write their findings on p. 369 of their *Science Notebooks*.

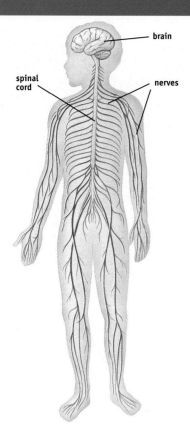

brain

spinal cord

nerves

▲ The brain is the control center for the nervous system. Nerves connect the brain to all parts of the body.

Side Trips Optional

You could end your tour here, since you've visited the three main parts of the brain. Or you could keep on going, following the path of a nerve impulse out of the brain. First, you would travel through the spinal cord. From there, you could choose any number of nerves that lead to all of the other parts of the body.

"Next stop, spinal column. After that, we head down to the toes." Good luck. You've got a long, exciting journey ahead of you! ■

INVESTIGATE FURTHER!

TAKE ACTION

The brain can become injured, just as other parts of the body can. But when the brain is injured, the effects can also show up in other parts of the body. Interview a doctor or nurse to find out about the consequences of head injuries. What are some of the best ways for you to avoid head injuries?

━━ INVESTIGATION 1 ━━

THINK IT WRITE IT

1. Compare the functions of the three main parts of the brain.

2. A skier had a severe injury to her lower back, damaging the spinal cord. As a result, her legs and feet are paralyzed. Explain her condition, based on what you've learned about the nervous system.

G33

Assessment

Portfolio

Describe a Job You are a manager cell in the nervous system. Write a job description for a neuron. Include all the qualities that a good neuron should have for optimum performance on the team.

Investigation Review
What Role Do the Brain and Nerves Play?

Name _____ Date _____

1. Draw a line to match each part of the nervous system with the job that it does.

a. motor neurons — receive stimuli from the environment
b. medulla — part of the brain that controls heartbeat rate
c. spinal cord — path that nerve impulses travel to and from the brain
d. sensory neurons — travels at 120 meters per second
e. nerve impulse — part of the brain that controls muscles and coordination
f. cerebrum — give signals for muscles to respond
g. cerebellum — part of the brain related to thinking and emotions

2. For each example, write *sensory* or *motor* for the type of neuron that would carry the message through your body.

a. You hear your favorite song. ___sensory___
b. You start dancing. ___motor___
c. You step on your bike pedal. ___motor___
d. You smell something burning. ___sensory___
e. You pull socks out of a drawer. ___motor___

Process Skills
Predicting

Joe is learning to drive a car. During his third drive, a dog steps into the road. It takes Joe two seconds to step on the brake. How much time would it take him to respond to the same thing after he had been driving several months? Why?

Students should predict that it will take less time to respond once Joe has had some practice driving.

INVESTIGATION 1
Close
the Investigation

Critical Thinking Skills
Applying, Analyzing

1. The cerebrum interprets information from the environment and controls the actions of different parts of the body. It allows people to think and make decisions and is where emotions and attitudes originate. The cerebellum coordinates muscles of the body and provides a sense of balance. The medulla controls the involuntary actions of the body.

2. The spinal cord is the passageway for nerve impulses to and from the brain. Damage to the spinal cord could interfere with the transport of these messages.

Challenge Students can compare the nervous system to a computer system. Suggest that they make diagrams comparing both systems, showing how both receive, process, transmit, and store information. Activity Support Master "Compare-Contrast Diagram" (TRB p. 68) might also be helpful to students.

Following Up

Baseline Assessment Return to the descriptions that students wrote at the beginning of the investigation. Ask students to interpret what happened based on their new knowledge of the nervous system.

Reteaching Draw a simple diagram of the human body, with the brain, eyes, and feet clearly depicted. Tell students that this person has just seen a car accident and is going to run for help. Invite students to tell you the process by which the legs begin to move while you draw arrows on the body.

📓 Use *Science Notebook* p. 370.

◄ **Investigation Review**
Use Investigation Review p. 166 in the *Assessment Guide*.

How Can You Respond to Things Around You?

Planner

Subconcept The sense receptors collect information from the environment for the brain to interpret and respond to; reflexes allow the nervous system to respond to danger automatically.

Objectives

- **Infer** how someone learns and remembers.
- **Compare** reflex actions to voluntary actions.
- **Investigate** the five sense organs.
- **Describe** the stages of mental development.

Pacing 4–5 class periods

Science Terms receptors, taste buds, optic nerve, auditory nerve, reflex

Activate Prior Knowledge

Baseline Assessment Students can list ten different stimuli they have learned to recognize. Keep the lists for use in Following Up.

Activity — Test Your Mind

Preview *Students play a memory game and should find that their ability improves with practice.*

1. Get Ready

Time about 30 minutes

Grouping pairs

Materials Hints Use Activity Support Masters G2 and G3 TRB (pp. G65–G66).

Multi-Age Strategy Let students practice using the timer. This will give multi-age pairs a chance to become more effective teams. Point out to pairs that they are not competing against each other; they are finding out if they can improve their own times in this memory game.

How Can You Respond to Things Around You?

It's time for lunch! You smell food and hear laughter from the lunchroom. Hungry kids bump into you as they join the line. You eye the choices and decide on a bowl of soup. Find out how the senses work with your nerves and brain to respond to all the choices in your environment.

Activity
Test Your Mind

MATERIALS
- index cards
- marker
- timer
- *Science Notebook*

How does the brain get the information it needs to learn and remember? Try this activity to find out how memory is related to how quickly you respond.

Procedure

1. With a marker, write a large letter *A* on one side of an index card. Do the same for the letters *B* through *F*. Then make another set of cards to match the first. You will have six pairs of cards when finished.

2. Have a partner mix up the cards and lay them on a table, letter-side down, in three neat rows of four cards each. Don't watch!

3. Your partner will tell you when to begin and will time you. You should select two cards to turn over, trying to match similar letters. If the cards don't match, place them face down in position again. When you make a match, leave the cards face up in their places.

Step 1

G34

Responding to Individual Needs

Students Acquiring English Demonstrate steps 3 and 4 for students and tell them to write down their own predictions in their *Science Notebooks* on p. 371. Students can work in pairs to elaborate on this matching game. One student from each pair can write, on five separate index cards, the words for the five senses. The other student can use five other index cards to illustrate each of the senses. The pair can then play the matching game together.

Step 3

4. Continue until you have matched all the pairs of cards. Record in a chart in your *Science Notebook* the time it took you to do this.

5. Predict what will happen when you do this test again with the cards in the same places. Record your prediction.

6. Repeat steps 3 and 4. Compare your times.

7. Now your partner will mix the cards around, keeping three rows. Predict what will happen when you do the test this time.

8. Repeat steps 3 and 4. Compare your times. Compare your data with the data of other groups.

Analyze and Conclude

1. In which case did you match all the letters in the shortest amount of time?

2. How did your time for the third test compare with your times for the other tests?

3. What role do you think learning and memory played in this activity? Tell what evidence you can cite to support your answer.

INVESTIGATE FURTHER!

EXPERIMENT

Make pairs of cards for six more letters and repeat the activity with six rows of four cards in each row. How do your times compare to those with twelve cards? Explain why this happened.

G35

Investigate Further

Experiment

Students might predict that they will show similar improvement, but that their times won't be as short as in the previous experiment because the task is more complex. Students should record their predictions and results in their *Science Notebooks* on p. 372.

---

2. Guide the Procedure

- Students should write each letter clearly and in the same style, so that it is easy to see whether or not two cards match.

- **Is there any luck involved in this activity? If so, how?** Yes, a player who gets a match on the first two cards turned over is lucky. Luck also comes into play every time a card is turned over that has not been turned before. But even this is not all luck; the player may not know where the matching card is, but he or she may know where it *isn't* by remembering the positions of other cards that were turned up.

 Have students record their measurements and predictions and answer questions on *Science Notebook* p. 371.

 Students could use the CD-ROM Spreadsheet to organize and display their data.

3. Assess Performance

Process Skills Checklist
- Did students accurately **record** their results after each of the trials?
- Were their **predictions** reasonable? Did they **predict** that they would improve with practice?
- Did they **infer** that learning was taking place as they played the game?

Analyze and Conclude
1. Most students will have the shortest time in the second test, when they have already seen the cards in those positions.

2. The time for the third test will likely be about the same as for the first test but longer than the second test.

3. Memory helps a person play well because the positions of the cards can be learned. Students should cite how well they did in each succeeding trial as evidence of these facts.

Activity  Reflex Action

Preview *Students focus on reflex responses and should find that the knee jerks lightly when tapped.*

1. Get Ready

Time about 15 minutes

Grouping pairs

 Collaborative Strategy Students may wish to work in groups of four to do this activity.

Safety Review safety precautions with students. Caution students to tap gently.

2. Guide the Procedure

- Tell students that they may need to tap in several places before they find the right spot on the knee that produces a response.

- **Has a doctor ever tapped your knee like this during a physical exam? What was the doctor testing for?** Reflexes

 Have students record their predictions and results, and answer questions on *Science Notebook* pp. 373–374.

Let students use the CD-ROM Spreadsheet and Grapher to organize and display their data.

3. Assess Performance

Process Skills Checklist

- Did students **predict** what would happen when their knees were tapped?

- Did students **record** predictions and results concerning their reflexes accurately?

- Did students **infer** how reflex actions differ from voluntary actions?

Analyze and Conclude

1. The lower leg kicked outward lightly. Some students may have predicted this; others may have said that they would simply feel the tap.

2. It is possible to partly, but not completely, control the reflex. Students may deduce that the reflex is controlled by a part of the brain that the conscious mind does not control.

3. Reflex actions, unlike other actions, cannot be controlled. Reflex actions allow one to respond to stimuli more quickly than do voluntary actions.

Activity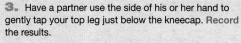
Reflex Action

Have you ever touched something hot and pulled your hand away before you felt any pain? This is another way your nervous system can respond to your environment.

Procedure

1. Sit in a chair and cross your legs so that the top leg can swing freely.

2. **Predict** what will happen if your top leg is gently tapped just below the kneecap. **Record** your prediction in your *Science Notebook*.

3. Have a partner use the side of his or her hand to gently tap your top leg just below the kneecap. **Record** the results.

4. Repeat step 3, but this time try to keep your top leg from moving.

Step 3

Analyze and Conclude

1. What happened to your leg when your partner tapped it? How did this compare to your prediction?

2. What happened when you concentrated on controlling your leg? Why did this happen?

3. A reflex is an automatic response that you can't control. In what ways do voluntary actions, which you can control, differ from reflex actions?

G36

Investigate Further

Responding to Individual Needs

Linguistic Activity Have students make a list of words that describe what happens to the leg when the knee is tapped. Record this list on the chalkboard or use Activity Support Master "Word Web" (TRB p. 70). Encourage students to use the list of words to create a poem that describes the difference between reflex and voluntary actions.

The Senses

Can you name your five senses? Reread the description on page G34 of standing in the lunch line and try to identify the senses. Your senses let you collect information from your environment. When your brain receives this information, it analyzes it and decides on the proper actions by your body.

Your senses work because of sense **receptors,** which are special sensory neurons that can receive stimuli from the environment. These receptors are found in your five sense organs—the skin, tongue, nose, eyes, and ears.

Touch

The skin is the body's largest organ. Your skin protects you, but it also provides you with your sense of touch. Under the skin's surface are receptors that can sense the texture of objects. Other receptors deeper in the skin sense pressure. Still other receptors sense heat, cold, and pain.

These receptors collect this information and pass it along to sensory neurons. The information reaches the brain through nerve impulses, as you saw in the diagram on page G29.

Receptors in the skin provide you with your sense of touch. ▼

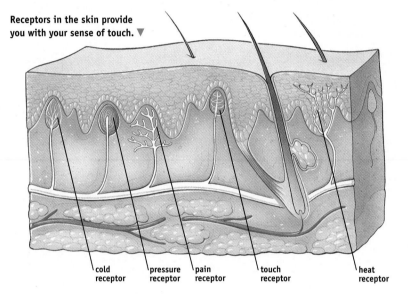

cold receptor   pressure receptor   pain receptor   touch receptor   heat receptor

G37

Investigate Further

Integrating the Sciences

PHYSICAL SCIENCE

What to Do Gather four plastic bowls. Fill one bowl with cold water, one with warm water, and two bowls with water at room temperature. Allow students to work in groups to take turns placing one hand in a bowl of cold water and simultaneously placing the other hand in a bowl of warm water for 30 seconds. Right afterwards, have the student place each hand in a bowl filled with room-temperature water. Students should predict how each hand will feel.

What's the Result? Discuss students' predictions. They should find that the hand that was in cold water felt warmer in room-temperature water than the hand that was previously in the warm water. Explain that the brain compared each sensation of temperature to the last and so interpreted the temperature of the water differently for each hand.

The Senses

Preview *Students focus on the five sense organs and how they transmit information to the brain.*

1. Get Ready

Science Terms receptors, taste buds, optic nerve, auditory nerve

Background

- In addition to the five main senses, a person can also sense the relative positions of parts of his or her body. This is called the proprioceptive, or kinesthetic, sense. This sense enables a person to close his or her eyes, hold the arms out to the side, and bring the forefingers together. This inner sense of position is also what enables a typist to know the position of the keys on a keyboard without looking at them.

- The retina is made up of two kinds of light receptor cells—rods and cones. Rods are stimulated by dim light and allow one to see black, white, and gray. Cones are stimulated by bright light and allow one to see color.

Discussion Starter

- **What is your favorite flavor? Your favorite color? Your favorite music? What do taste, sight, and sound have in common?** They are ways we sense the world around us.

- **How do you think the brain receives information from the various sense organs, such as the ears, tongue, and skin?** Stimuli such as sounds, foods, and pressure on the skin activate nerve impulses that send messages to the brain.

2. Guide the Discussion

Choose from the following strategies to facilitate discussion.

Connecting to the Activities

- ***Reflex Action, p. G36***
  How did your body respond to the sense of touch in the activity? The lower leg moved slightly upward.

- ■ **Why do you think your leg responded in the way that it did?** The spinal column received a message in response to the tap and relayed a message for the involuntary response of the leg.

Drawing Conclusions

- **People can feel pain and pressure on organs that are inside the body. What do internal organs have that allow these feelings?** Sensory receptors

- ■ **Why do you think it is important for these organs, as well as your skin, to have pain receptors?** These receptors allow a person to determine if something is wrong internally; if there were no sensory receptors, a person might not know if there was a problem with an internal organ.

Thinking Critically

■ **How might the other senses of a visually impaired person be different from those of a person without visual impairment?** Students might say the other senses become keener. As an example, show students a sample of Braille. Let students run their fingers over the raised bumps. **Can you distinguish one group of bumps from another well enough to read them?** Probably not. But students might point out that with practice, their sense of touch would become sensitive enough to use Braille.

Making Inferences

■ **What do you think happens if you hold your nose while you eat something?** It is more difficult to determine the flavor of the food. **Why?** Your senses of smell and taste are connected. If you hold your nose, or if you have a cold, information about the food's smell does not get to the brain.

Taste

Your sense of taste is centered in your tongue, which has taste receptors on its surface. These receptors are bunched together in small round bumps called **taste buds.** Most taste buds lie on the tip and back of the tongue.

Your taste buds only respond to four basic tastes: bitter, sour, sweet, and salty. The many combinations of these four tastes produce the wide variety of tastes you experience.

Smell

Your sense of smell results from receptors in your nose that sense chemical particles floating in the air. These receptors have tiny hairs that extend into the air passages in your nose.

When they sense chemicals, the receptors send nerve impulses to a smell center in the brain. The brain uses its memory bank and interprets these nerve impulses from the nose as odors, or smells.

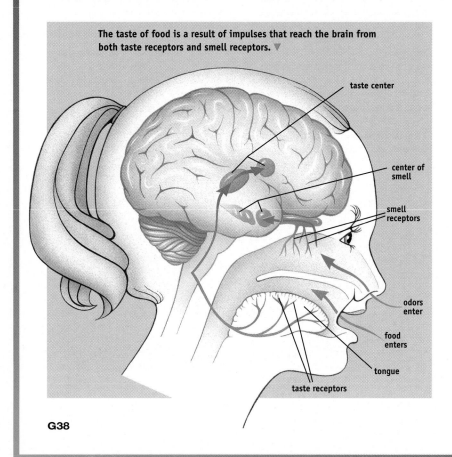

The taste of food is a result of impulses that reach the brain from both taste receptors and smell receptors. ▼

taste center

center of smell

smell receptors

odors enter

food enters

tongue

taste receptors

G38

Investigate Further

Cultural Connection

TESTING TASTE **What to Do** Students can investigate how the senses of taste and smell work together, while at the same time they experience the many flavors of foods from different lands. Encourage students to bring into class samples of ethnic foods that they enjoy eating. Let volunteers taste the food first while holding their nose, and then taste the food again without holding their nose. Ask students to note any differences they find between the two taste tests.

What's the Result? Students should find that their sense of taste was heightened when they did not hold their nose. Guide a class discussion in which students conclude that the sense of taste and the sense of smell work together.

Sight

Your sense of sight—your vision—is a result of sense receptors within your eyes. These receptors gather information from light rays.

Light enters the eye through the lens, which focuses an image on the surface of the retina (ret''n ə), at the back of the eye. The light affects receptors on the retina, producing nerve impulses. These nerve impulses travel to the brain along a bundle of neurons called the **optic nerve**. So you actually "see" with your brain.

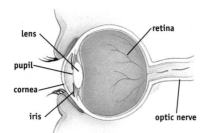

▲ Light rays are focused by the lens onto the retina. Receptors sense the light and send impulses to the brain through the optic nerve.

Hearing

Your sense of hearing is a result of receptors in your ears. These receptors sense vibrations in the air.

Sounds are really vibrations that move through the air in waves. Your outer ear collects these sound waves and funnels them in through your ear canal. At the end of the ear canal is a membrane called the eardrum, which vibrates with the sound waves. These vibrations are passed into the inner ear, where receptors turn them into nerve impulses. The impulses travel to the brain through the **auditory nerve.** Your brain interprets these impulses as sound. ■

Your ears are organs that can translate sound waves into nerve impulses. ▼

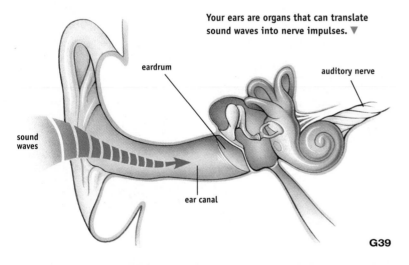

G39

Integrating the Curriculum

Science & Social Studies

USING SENSES

What to Do Have students work in groups to cut out magazine pictures of people using their five senses. Direct students to glue each picture onto a sheet of paper. Then have them examine each picture and list near the picture all the ways in which the senses are being used in that picture, as well as the stimulus for that sense.

What's the Result? Ask groups to think of ways in which the five senses link people from many lands. Students should conclude that people all over the world share the experience of touch, taste, smell, hearing, and sight. Groups can then work together to assemble all of their pictures and construct separate books for each of the senses to donate to the classroom or school library.

Making Inferences

- **What must be present in order for you to see?** Light must be present. **How do you see most things?** Most objects are seen because they reflect light, not give it off or produce it. Exceptions include objects that do actually give off light, such as light bulbs, the Sun, and other stars.

Drawing Conclusions

How does the shape of the ear help you hear? The funnel shape helps collect sound waves, directing them into the ear canal.

Thinking Critically

How can you demonstrate that sounds are vibrations? Students could place a hand to the side of the face and neck as they speak. They will be able to feel the sound waves vibrating the tissues.

Drawing Conclusions

- **What might happen if someone has damaged the optic nerve or the auditory nerve? Why?** A person's ability to see or hear would be impaired because the nerve impulses could not travel to the brain where they would be interpreted as sights and sounds.

Responding to Individual Needs

Students Acquiring English Provide a simple drawing of the body with the five senses labeled at points on the body. Students can make a list of five items that relate to each of the five senses. For example, for taste they can write five foods, for sound they can write five sounds that they hear, and so on.

3. Assess Understanding

Write the names of numerous sensory stimuli—chocolate ice cream, perfume, velvet, bright light, and drumming, for example—on small slips of paper, and put one for each of the five senses in an envelope. Divide the class into groups of five. Provide an envelope for each of the groups. Each student will reach into the envelope, draw a slip of paper, and read the item out loud. He or she can then name which sense the item corresponds to and briefly explain to the group how the stimulus is carried by a sensory neuron to the brain. Note: Some stimuli may involve the response of more than one sense.

Stages of Mental Development

Preview *Students focus on five stages of mental development during childhood.*

1. Get Ready

Background

- Early childhood is marked by rapid growth, but the most phenomenal development in these years is language acquisition—first by our increase in vocabulary and word combinations and later by our understanding of complex syntax and grammar. In early childhood, we also learn to use symbols and language to manipulate the environment. In middle childhood, we begin to use logic, time, and numbers, and our memory capacity expands. Both short- and long-term memory and speed of recall improve steadily between the ages of 7 and 12.

Discussion Starter

- **Do you have younger brothers or sisters? What can you do that they haven't mastered yet?** Students should mention a variety of physical abilities. Some will be quite obvious if there is an age difference of several years. Age differences of only a year or so will yield more subtle differences in abilities.

- **Name a mental activity you can do now that you couldn't do two years ago.** Students may say they can do math calculations in their head, or that they can more easily remember things that they study.

2. Guide the Discussion

Choose from the following strategies to facilitate the discussion.

Connecting to the Activities

- *Test Your Mind, p. G34*
  Do you think you'd be better at playing the card game than someone who was several years younger? Why? Memory and learning abilities develop during childhood. An older child probably has a more fully developed ability to memorize and learn.

Stages of Mental Development

Stages of Mental Development

You've grown quite a bit in the last few years. You're probably much stronger now than you were in the second grade, and you can do things today that you couldn't do before.

Your brain has been growing along with the rest of your body. As you experience more of life and as your brain grows, you gain the ability to think in more complex ways. This process has been going on since you were born.

Everyone is different, and each person's mental abilities develop in different ways. But in some ways we're all alike. We all gain certain mental abilities at about the same stage of life, as you can see in this time line.

Remember, every person develops differently in both physical and mental abilities. Because you're still growing, you can be sure that some things you can't do or understand now will become easier as you grow older. Isn't it nice to know you have things to look forward to!

When a baby is born, its brain has already been growing for nine months. Although the brain will grow much more, even a newborn has an active, exploring mind.

BIRTH

INFANCY
In the first few months of life, a baby is aware only of its immediate surroundings. When something disappears from view, it's just gone—the baby has no understanding that things exist apart from what he or she sees. Therefore, to develop fully, an infant needs to be provided with a rich and varied environment.

G40

Investigate Further

Cultural Connection

RITES OF AGE

What to Do Share with students that many cultures have special ceremonies to welcome their children into adulthood when they reach a certain age. For example, some Hispanic communities hold a *quinceañera* to celebrate a girl's 15th birthday. In the Southwest, Mescalero Apache girls ages 12 to 14 go through a four-day ritual that includes dancing and singing. Afterwards, a young woman is expected to take on adult responsibilities. Encourage students to write about new responsibilities they now have and expect to take on in the future.

What's the Result? Invite volunteers to share their ideas. **What are some signs in our society that a young person has reached adulthood?** Students may mention getting their driver's license and registering to vote.

Children become much more logical at this stage of mental development. They begin to better understand concepts such as time and geography. They not only can find their way around but also can draw a map for others to use. They can now predict how others might think or feel in a situation.

MIDDLE CHILDHOOD

LATE CHILDHOOD

When a young person reaches this stage, he or she can think in terms of symbols and can solve complex mental problems. A person at this stage can approach a problem by forming hypotheses—and testing those hypotheses in a logical way. This is also when a person can begin to reflect upon his or her own life and thoughts.

EARLY CHILDHOOD

As children pass into this stage of life, they master language ability. Using language, they can talk and think about the past—and anticipate the future. This is the time when a child seems always to be asking, "Why?" Children are discovering the world, though at this stage they think the world revolves around them.

UNIT PROJECT LINK

Just as there are stages of mental development, your body too develops over time. And all physical activities are controlled by the nervous system. With your group, think of a physical activity that demonstrates the coordination of the skeletal and muscular systems by the nervous system. The activity should be challenging but not impossible. Make a flowchart to show the pathways of nerve impulses during the activity.

G41

Unit Project Link

Student groups should each plan a competitive physical activity that demonstrates the coordination of the skeletal and muscular systems by the nervous system. These activities should be something that challenges students, but are still possible to do. On p. 375 of their *Science Notebooks*, each group should describe the activity and make a flowchart to reflect the pathways of nerve impulses during its activity. You may also have students use Unit Project Master G4 (TRB p. 111).

Thinking About the Data

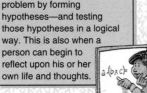 Together with students, read the caption about middle childhood. **How do you know when a child can understand concepts such as time and geography? How old were you when you were able to tell a friend how to get to your home?** Students should answer from their own experiences.

Making Comparisons

How do the descriptions of the stages of mental development compare to your own observations? Students will notice some variability. Stress that everyone is unique and develops in his or her own way, but there will likely be more agreement with the descriptions of the stages than disagreement.

Responding to Individual Needs

Linguistic Activity Have students work in small groups to make up a fictitious story for younger children about a baby animal growing up. Let them tell their story to a kindergarten or pre-school class, and have the students ask the children to make pictures to accompany the story.

3. Assess Understanding

 Students can work in small groups to discuss the following questions. **Does it make sense to try to start teaching math and reading to children at two years of age? Will a child be "smarter" and better educated if you start this teaching early?** Have students compare their responses with those of other groups. Starting school is seen in itself as a major development in children's lives. Most experts agree that learning to read and write at this age is not so much a new development as it is an opportunity to focus earlier achievements. Opinions differ over the most appropriate age at which to start teaching most children reading and number skills.

The Path of a Reflex

Preview *Students focus on the path of a nerve impulse during a reflex action.*

1. Get Ready

Science Term   reflex

Background

- Millions of temperature sensors are set deep in the dermis of the skin, and each receptor is one of several types. Krause's bulb is a temperature sensor thought to detect cold. Ruffini's organ, which helps detect heat and perhaps heavy pressure, causes a person to jerk a part of the body away from a heat source.

Discussion Starter

- **What are some examples of reflex actions?** The knee jerk, blinking, quickly pulling away from a heat source, coughing, gagging

- **How do these reflexes help you?** By preventing dangerously long exposure to harmful situations

2. Guide the Discussion

Use the following strategy to facilitate discussion.

Connecting to the Activities

- *Measuring Reaction Time, p. G27*
  Think back to how long it took you to catch a meterstick. Now think about accidentally putting your hand on a hot stove. If your hand were touching the stove for as long as it took to catch the stick, what would happen to it? It would get badly burned.

3. Assess Understanding

Tell students to draw a stick figure of a person whose hand has just touched a sharp thorn. They can trace the path of the nerve impulses to the spinal cord and back to the hand.

The Path of a Reflex

In Investigation 1 you learned about the path a nerve impulse takes—from a sensory neuron to the spinal cord, to the brain, and then back to a motor neuron. But sometimes there isn't time to think about the action. In those cases, the body responds with a **reflex,** or an automatic reaction to a stimulus.

You investigated your own reflexes in the activity on page G36. Now compare the path of a reflex, pictured below, with the path of a nerve impulse, shown on page G29. The boy's brain is informed that he has taken this reflex action, because another nerve impulse goes up the spinal cord to his brain. But in this instance the brain isn't involved in pulling the hand away.

Can you see why reflexes are important for our survival? Reflexes protect our bodies from harm by allowing us to quickly react to pain or danger. ■

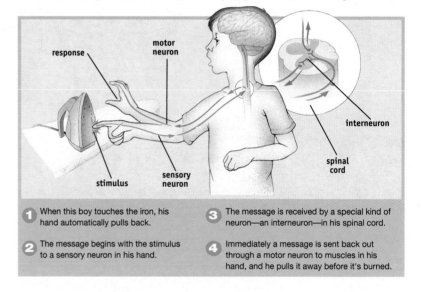

1. When this boy touches the iron, his hand automatically pulls back.

2. The message begins with the stimulus to a sensory neuron in his hand.

3. The message is received by a special kind of neuron—an interneuron—in his spinal cord.

4. Immediately a message is sent back out through a motor neuron to muscles in his hand, and he pulls it away before it's burned.

G42

Integrating the Curriculum

Science & Language Arts

What to Do Invite students to write a descriptive paragraph about what would happen if people didn't have reflexes. Students can focus on one situation and build a story around it.

What's the Result? Encourage students to share their stories. Allow others to add to the stories. Discuss any examples of reflexes that haven't been brought up in the stories or paragraphs.

Multi-Age Classroom Different students will be able to develop paragraphs and stories to different degrees. Reinforce the positive aspects of the writing, but don't overlook inaccuracies of grammar and sentence construction.

Brain Power

 As you've already read, nerve impulses are electrical in nature. Neurons have a chemical makeup that gives them the ability to send nerve impulses. The brain contains billions of neurons, and they all produce nerve impulses. In fact, the nerve impulses from your brain—called brain waves—can be measured and recorded by machines. Doctors often record brain waves if they think a patient may have an illness that has affected the brain.

▲ Doctors measure brain waves to discover the source of some illnesses.

Using Brain Waves

Some scientists are now working to develop ways to use brain waves in performing simple tasks. This notion may not be so far-fetched. This task involves using a machine to detect brain waves and having a computer respond by signaling electricity to flow.

The first difficulty faced by these scientists has been to figure out how to identify just the brain waves for a specific action. The brain produces so many impulses—so many things are going on at once in a person's head—that it's not clear which brain wave is connected to which mental activity.

Recording Brain Waves

To record brain waves, scientists attach a number of electrodes to a person's head. Electrodes are small metal disks that can pick up electric currents. Wires connect the electrodes to a piece of machinery.

With practice, some people have actually been able to direct a piece of machinery to do certain tasks, such as

G43

Investigate Further

FUTURE FIRSTS **What to Do** One of the main reasons researchers are working on brain-actuated control is to develop technology for people who have no use of their muscles. But entertainment is another area in which this research is likely to create enthusiasm. Already, people have used brain-actuated control to change channels on a television set, play a video game, and play a three-piece band just by thinking. Challenge students to think of some other possibilities for brain-actuated control and to make a list of their ideas.

What's the Result? Have students share their lists with the class. Choose the most plausible examples from the lists, and have students work in groups to make a poster advertising one of these brain-actuated controls. Create a bulletin-board display with the posters.

Brain Power

Preview *Students focus on the electrical aspect of nerve impulses and on a possible future technology that could make use of them.*

1. Get Ready

Background

- The actual time it takes us to sense something and respond to it is about seven hundredths of a second. Because different types of mental activities put out brain waves of different frequencies, a computer called a "signal processor" can be programmed to "listen" for particular frequencies. Using the fastest available signal processor, brain waves have been used to operate computer flight simulators with a delay of only about twenty hundredths of a second.

Discussion Starter

What are some real things today that might have seemed like "magic" or science fiction 20 years ago? 100 years ago? 20 years ago, virtual reality; 100 years ago, computers and space flight.

2. Guide the Discussion

Use the following strategy to facilitate discussion.

Connecting to the Activities

- *Measuring Reaction Time, p. G27*
  If the brain waves you generated in this activity could be measured and somehow turned into words, what would they say? They might say: "I see a meterstick. I know it's falling. I am planning to catch it. It's falling. There — I caught it."

3. Assess Understanding

 Students in small groups can summarize how brain waves could be used to operate a wheelchair. They should identify actions a motor-driven wheelchair must be able to do, devices needed to accomplish each action, and finally what commands need be given mentally to each device.

Close the Investigation

THINK IT WRITE IT

Critical Thinking Skills
Analyzing, Synthesizing, Evaluating, Applying

1. Sensory organs such as the eyes, ears, skin, nose, and mouth allow people to respond to the environment. Stimuli are picked up by sensory receptors; impulses then travel along nerve endings to the brain; the brain then sends out nerve impulses so the body responds in the appropriate ways.

2. If a person did not respond to a simple reflex test, it may indicate a problem with the functioning of the nervous system.

Challenge Students can investigate the different kinds of taste buds and where they are located on the tongue. Then students can work in groups to devise an experiment that tests the sensitivity of these different areas to different tastes.

Following Up

Baseline Assessment Return to the class lists of stimuli that the brain processes. Summarize how the brain receives these different pieces of information. Then ask students if they would like to add anything to the list.

Reteaching Draw a circle on the board to represent the brain. Students can create a word web around it, listing the kinds of information that the brain receives and sends out, with arrows indicating the destinations of the messages. You may wish to provide students with Activity Support Master "Word Web" (TRB p. 70).

 Use *Science Notebook* p. 376.

Investigation Review ▶
Use Investigation Review p. 167 in the *Assessment Guide*.

---

making a line on a computer screen. The scientists are not sure exactly which impulses from the brain are actually causing the computer to respond and the task to be done. But one thing is clear: Sometimes a thought can be used to direct the action of a machine.

▼ **"Look, Mom, no hands!"** Could this be you in the not-too-distant future?

Brain-Actuated Technology
What these scientists have been developing is called brain-actuated

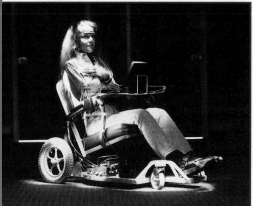

technology, meaning the machines used are directed by brain waves. The first application of this technology may be in devices for people who have lost the use of parts of their bodies. If a wheelchair could be steered by brain waves, then a person without the use of arms and legs could live a much fuller life. If this technology is perfected, the future might see all kinds of fantastic technologies. Imagine flying a plane just by thinking about what the plane should do! ■

▲ **A brain-actuated wheelchair would be a tremendous help to someone who has lost control of the arms and legs.**

INVESTIGATION 2

THINK IT WRITE IT

1. Describe how your nervous system allows you to sense your environment and respond to it. What are the major organs involved?

2. In a physical examination a doctor usually uses a small rubber mallet to test a patient's reflexes. Explain why you think this procedure is important in assessing a person's health.

G44

Assessment

Investigation Review
How Can You Respond to Things Around You?

Name _____ **Date** _____

1. Give an example of how the students in the picture experience each of the five senses.
Touch—warm popcorn. Hearing—popcorn popping. Sight—see popcorn. Smell—popcorn and butter. Taste—popcorn, butter, salt.

2. Write the stage of mental development described in each situation.
   a. Lucy can find her way home from school. She can draw a map of her neighborhood, and she understands the concepts of time and geography. Lucy is in __middle childhood__.
   b. Jessie is asking "Why?" all the time. She can now use language to talk and think about the past and future. Though she is learning to share, it is difficult because she thinks the world revolves around her. Jessie is in __early childhood__.
   c. Brendan's brain has already been growing for nine months. His mind is very active and it will continue to grow much more. Brendan is in the __birth__ stage of development.
   d. Claire can solve complex problems by forming a hypothesis and testing the hypothesis in a logical way. She also often thinks about her own thoughts and life as she discovers more about herself. Claire is in __late childhood__.

Process Skills
Predicting Suppose someone throws a snowball toward your face. How would you respond? Is your response voluntary or automatic? Write your answer on a separate sheet of paper. You might blink, which is an automatic reflex. You might move your hand to block the snowball or move your head away, both of which are voluntary responses.

Performance

In My Opinion Students can pretend they are scientists specializing in detecting and making use of nerve impulses. They can develop an argument in favor of government funding for brain-wave research and present it to a congressional committee made up of four or five of their classmates.

REFLECT & EVALUATE

WORD POWER

auditory nerve	neurons
cerebellum	receptors
cerebrum	reflex
medulla	stimuli
motor neurons	
nerve impulse	
optic nerve	
sensory neurons	
taste buds	

 On Your Own
Review the terms in the list. Then use as many terms as you can to make a labeled diagram of the nervous system.

 With a Partner
Write a clue for each term in the list. Then design a crossword puzzle, using the terms. Trade puzzles with your partner.

PORTFOLIO

Draw a diagram of the brain. Label each part and tell what it does.

Analyze Information

Study the drawing. Then describe the path of a nerve impulse during a reflex. Compare this path with the normal path of a nerve impulse.

Assess Performance

Design an experiment to measure reaction time when there are distracting noises. Work with a partner to carry out the experiment. Compare your results to the results from the activity on page G27.

Problem Solving

1. The brain is one of the best-protected organs in the body. Why is this protection important?

2. Dogs have a very keen sense of smell, and bats have highly developed hearing. Which senses are most developed in humans? How are these an advantage? Which senses are not so highly developed? How are these a disadvantage?

3. Reflexes are a means for your body to protect itself. Imagine that you don't have reflexes. What are some things that could happen to you?

G45

REFLECT & EVALUATE

Word Power

 On Your Own Students' diagrams should include terms related to the nervous system.

With a Partner Students' puzzle clues should reflect an understanding of the terms.

Analyze Information

The message goes from sensory neurons in the boy's fingers to an interneuron in his spinal cord. The interneuron quickly sends a message through a motor neuron back to muscles in his hand, telling them to pull away from the iron. This reflex reaction protects his hand. Normal impulses travel from a sense organ along sensory neurons to the spinal cord and then to the brain. The brain decides what to do and then sends a message along the motor neurons to the appropriate muscles.

Assess Performance

Evaluate students' ability to predict and test that distracting noise will increase response time.

Problem Solving

1. The brain is important to protect because it controls the body, allowing us to move, breathe, think, and learn.

2. A person's sight and hearing are better developed to give a person's brain information about our environment. While humans usually do not rely on senses to help them catch food or escape from predators, the senses of smell and taste can help them detect spoiled food.

3. A person might suffer serious injuries if he or she did not react by blinking, coughing, or responding quickly.

Use *Science Notebook* pp. 377–378.

PORTFOLIO

Students' diagrams of the brain should show the information included in the illustrations on pp. G30, G31, and G38.

Chapter Test   pp. 168–169 in the Assessment Guide

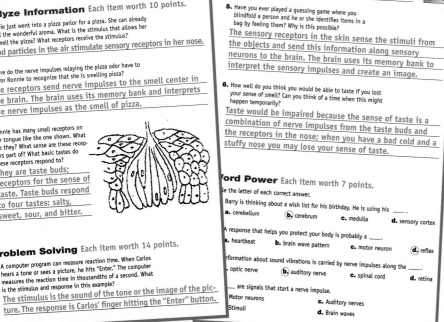

Chapter Test
The Nervous System

CHAPTER 2

Name _____ Date _____

Analyze Information Each item worth 10 points.

1. Ronnie just went into a pizza parlor for a pizza. She can already smell the wonderful aroma. What is the stimulus that allows her to smell the pizza? What receptors receive the stimulus?
Food particles in the air stimulate sensory receptors in her nose.

2. Where do the nerve impulses relaying the pizza odor have to go for Ronnie to recognize that she is smelling pizza?
The receptors send nerve impulses to the smell center in the brain. The brain uses its memory bank and interprets the nerve impulses as the smell of pizza.

3. Ronnie has many small receptors on her tongue like the one shown. What are they? What sense are these receptors part of? What basic tastes do these receptors respond to?
They are taste buds; receptors for the sense of taste. Taste buds respond to four tastes: salty, sweet, sour, and bitter.

Problem Solving Each item worth 14 points.

4. A computer program can measure reaction time. When Carlos hears a tone or sees a picture, he hits "Enter." The computer measures the reaction time in thousandths of a second. What is the stimulus and response in this example?
The stimulus is the sound of the tone or the image of the picture. The response is Carlos' finger hitting the "Enter" button.

Chapter Test
The Nervous System

CHAPTER 2

Name _____ Date _____

5. Have you ever played a guessing game where you blindfold a person and he or she identifies items in a bag by feeling them? Why is this possible?
The sensory receptors in the skin sense the stimuli from the objects and send this information along sensory neurons to the brain. The brain uses its memory bank to interpret the sensory impulses and create an image.

6. How well do you think you would be able to taste if you lost your sense of smell? Can you think of a time when this might happen temporarily?
Taste would be impaired because the sense of taste is a combination of nerve impulses from the taste buds and the receptors in the nose; when you have a bad cold and a stuffy nose you may lose your sense of taste.

Word Power Each item worth 7 points.
Circle the letter of each correct answer.

Barry is thinking about a wish list for his birthday. He is using his ___.
a. cerebellum   **b.** cerebrum   **c.** medulla   **d.** sensory cortex

A response that helps you protect your body is probably a ___.
a. heartbeat   **b.** brain wave pattern   **c.** motor neuron   **d.** reflex

Information about sound vibrations is carried by nerve impulses along the ___.
a. optic nerve   **b.** auditory nerve   **c.** spinal cord   **d.** retina

___ are signals that start a nerve impulse.
a. Motor neurons   **c.** Auditory nerves
b. Stimuli   **d.** Brain waves

CHAPTER 3

STAYING IN CONTROL

Subconcepts	Activities	Materials
Investigation 1 How Do Drugs Affect the Body?		

The misuse of drugs, substances that can affect the function of cells and tissues, can cause harmful changes in the body that can endanger a person's safety and long-term health.
 	
Suggested Pacing: 2–3 class periods
Standards
    p. 168
Benchmarks
    pp. 11, 144
	Ad Power, p. G48
	Science Processes: classify; communicate; collect, record, and interpret data
		posterboard, marker*, magazines, scissors, paste or tape, *Science Notebook* pp. 381–382

Investigation 2 How Does Alcohol Affect the Body?		

Alcohol has harmful short- and long-term effects on the body and is responsible for many accidents and deaths.
 	
Suggested Pacing: 1–2 class periods
Standards
    p. 168
Benchmarks
    pp. 11, 144
	Alcohol Advertising: Pro and Con, p. G56
	Science Processes: communicate, predict
		reference articles and other resources with which students can research both sides of the argument, *Science Notebook* pp. 386–387

Overview

In this chapter students will discover the persuasiveness of advertisements and will learn about the misuse of drugs. Students will also examine the effects of alcohol on the body and on a person's ability to drive.

Chapter Concept

The use of tobacco, alcohol, and other drugs can cause harmful effects to the systems of the body.

Advance Preparation	Curriculum Connection	Assessment
Ad Power Collect discarded magazines that have advertisements for medicines, alcohol, and tobacco products. Review students' survey questions before groups carry out their surveys. Survey questions should not be too personal; participants should remain anonymous.	Math TG p. G50 Social Studies TG p. G52 Science, Technology, & Society TG p. G54	**Chapter 3 Baseline Assessment:** *Science Notebook* pp. 379–380 **Investigation 1 Baseline Assessment:** TG p. G48 **Investigation 1 Review:** AG p. 170 **Think It/Write It,** p. G55; *Science Notebook* p. 385 **Following Up on Baseline Assessment:** TG p. G55 **Portfolio:** TG p. G55
Alcohol Advertising: Pro and Con Gather research materials regarding alcohol use and its advertising. You might find information in books, pamphlets, newspapers, and magazines.	Language Arts TG p. G58 Cultural Connection TG p. G59 Literature TG p. G60 Integrating the Sciences TG p. G60 Social Studies TG p. G61	**Investigation 2 Baseline Assessment:** TG p. G56 **Investigation 2 Review:** AG p. 171 **Think It/Write It,** p. G62; *Science Notebook* p. 388 **Following Up on Baseline Assessment:** TG p. G62 **Performance:** TG p. G62 **Chapter 3 Summative Assessment** Reflect and Evaluate, p. G63 Chapter 3 Review/Test: AG pp. 172–173 *Science Notebook* pp. 389–390

TG= Teaching Guide   TRB= Teacher Resource Book   AG= Assessment Guide   *Materials in Equipment Kit

CHAPTER 3 Introducing the Chapter

Chapter Overview

Chapter Concept The use of tobacco, alcohol, and other drugs can cause harmful effects to the systems of the body.

Theme: Systems

Drugs can affect the function of body cells, tissues, organs, and systems. Drug abuse may cause damage to several systems, particularly the nervous, circulatory, respiratory, and digestive systems.

Common Misconceptions

Students may think nicotine and alcohol are legal drugs that they can use. They will learn that it is *not* legal for young people to use tobacco or alcohol, *even* though adults may legally use both drugs.

Options for Setting the Stage

Warm-Up Activity

Ask students to list three reasons why smoking is not "cool." (Smoking is unhealthy, expensive, and illegal for young people.)

Discussion Starter:
Getting the Point

Use the photo and text to start a discussion about overcoming drug abuse.

 Use *Science Notebook* pp. 379–380.

- **The photo shows a person being treated with acupuncture, a process sometimes used successfully with drug addicts. How does this reveal that a drug addict loses control over his or her own body?** A person who is addicted to drugs often needs help to stay drug-free.

- **Career:** *Acupuncturist*
Tell students acupuncture began in China over 2,000 years ago. An acupuncturist inserts sharp needles at any of hundreds of specific points on the body to relieve pain, to treat conditions such as arthritis, asthma, migraine, and to reduce the craving for drugs. Some acupuncturists are accredited physicians educated in the United States who also have a certificate for practicing acupuncture.

CHAPTER 3 STAYING IN CONTROL

Drug abuse. What images come to your mind when you read this phrase? Perhaps you see a person who is out of control, ranting wildly. Or maybe you imagine a dazed person staring blankly into the distance. Now think about an ordinary drugstore and its over-the-counter and prescription medicines. Can even these legal drugs be abused?

Getting the Point

Sally Dan practices acupuncture (ak′yōō puŋk chər), an ancient Chinese technique. She uses thin needles to probe points on her patients' bodies. These points seem to be linked with certain functions, such as breathing, or with certain organs, such as the liver. Only a mild tingling or sometimes a stinging sensation is felt.

Acupuncture has long been used to treat pain. But today it also helps addicts break the habit of using heroin, cocaine, nicotine, or alcohol. Recent studies show that those addicts who use acupuncture along with regular rehabilitation techniques stay drug-free longer than those who do not.

Why would people put into their bodies substances that can block awareness and lead to life-threatening disease? What decisions will you make about your own use of drugs?

G46

Home-School Connection

The Explore at Home activity "A Drug Survey" encourages students to apply their knowledge and increase their awareness of drugs in their home environment. Distribute the activity (TRB p. 36) when students have completed the chapter. Ask students to list the drugs they came in contact with in their homes.

Explore at Home

Name _____ Date _____

A DRUG SURVEY

Drugs are effective only when taken as directed and provided that they have not expired. Drug manufacturers include expiration dates on their products. Taking or using medicines that were prescribed for someone else or that have expired can be both ineffective and dangerous.

Materials

✔ over-the-counter and prescription drugs
✔ other medications, such as ointments, used in your home

Procedure

Ask an adult family member to help you take an inventory of all the medications in your home. Use the Data Table below to record information on each medication. Include both prescription and over-the-counter drugs in your survey.

Results

Review the data you collected and indicate clearly which medications have expired. Call a local pharmacy to find out how to safely dispose of the expired medications and why expired medications are unsafe to use. Also ask why prescription drugs should be taken only by the person for whom they are prescribed and only as directed. Share your information with the rest of your family. Tape your findings to the inside of your medicine cabinet to remind family members to check the dates and dosages of all drugs used in your home.

Data Table			
Drug	Person(s) Who Use It	Date Prescribed	Expiration Date

How Do Drugs Affect the Body?
.... **G48**

How Does Alcohol Affect the Body?
.... **G56**

◄ Acupuncture points are found throughout the body.

G47

Technology Alert

CD-ROM

Tools: Spreadsheet; Writer; Painter

The Spreadsheet and Writer can be used to compare and contrast the legal and illegal drugs mentioned in the chapter as well as their effects on the human body. These same tools can also be used to chart the results of the activities Ad Power and Alcohol Advertising: Pro and Con. Students might also wish to use the Painter to create cartoons warning of the serious problems associated with drug abuse and misuse.

Chapter Road Map

How Do Drugs Affect the Body?

Activities
* Ad Power

Resources
* The Misuse of Drugs

Drugs and Sports

How Does Alcohol Affect the Body?

Activities
* Alcohol Advertising: Pro and Con

Resources
* Alcohol in the Body

Alcohol and Driving

*Pressed for Time?

As you work through the upcoming investigations, focus on the activities and resources identified by the clock.

Look for this symbol in front of questions that help develop Scientific Reasoning Skills.

How Do Drugs Affect the Body?

Planner

Subconcept The misuse of drugs, substances that can affect the function of cells and tissues, can cause harmful changes in the body that can endanger a person's safety and long-term health.

Objectives

- **Infer** how ads influence attitudes toward drugs.
- **Identify** types of drugs and their effects.
- **Describe** how some athletes use harmful drugs.

Pacing 2–3 class periods

Science Terms drug, caffeine, alcohol, nicotine, illegal drug, substance abuse, addiction, steroid, stimulant, narcotic

Activate Prior Knowledge

Baseline Assessment Students list all the drugs they can think of. Save lists for Following Up.

Activity Ad Power

Preview *Students conduct a survey of student attitudes towards medicines, tobacco, and alcohol, analyze magazine ads for drugs, and should find that ads attempt to make drug use desirable.*

Advance Preparation *See p. G46b.*

1. Get Ready

Time about 45 minutes

Grouping groups of 3–4

Collaborative Strategy As they work, some students could locate the ads while other group members work on writing the survey. All students should analyze the ads and make their own inferences.

How Do Drugs Affect the Body?

Many diseases that commonly killed people in the past are now easily treated with modern drugs. Drugs can be very helpful when they are properly used. What happens to the systems of the body when drugs are misused?

Activity

MATERIALS
- posterboard
- marker
- magazines
- scissors
- paste or tape
- *Science Notebook*

Ad Power

Both helpful drugs and harmful drugs are common in today's society. How do magazine advertisements influence people about drugs? Find out!

Procedure

1. Work in groups of three or four. In your *Science Notebook*, write survey questions to find out people's attitudes about taking medicines and about using tobacco and alcohol. Do people think medicines, alcohol, and tobacco are safe? Do people think these products are safe all the time?

2. With your group, survey ten students and tally the results. Then create a chart on posterboard. Show the result of each survey question.

Step 2

G48

 Responding to Individual Needs

Visual/Spatial Activity After students compare the ads, ask them to choose an ad that is most appealing to them. Encourage students to explain what makes the ad appealing. Then have students make their own ad that uses the same strategy. The ad should promote a healthful product, such as vitamins, healthful foods, or exercise equipment.

3. Look through magazines to find ten advertisements for medicines, alcohol, and tobacco products. Cut out the ads and display them on another piece of posterboard.

4. Show the ads to the same students you surveyed in step 2. Then ask them the survey questions again.

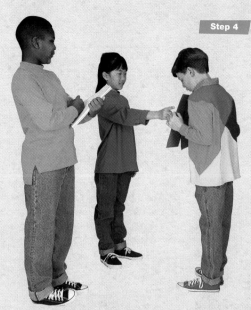

Step 4

5. Tally the results from the second survey and add them to the chart. **Compare** your data from the two surveys. **Discuss** your results with your group and other groups.

Analyze and Conclude

1. **Describe** the results of your first survey in your *Science Notebook*.

2. Did the results of your second survey differ from those of your first survey? If so, how?

3. Consider the methods the magazine advertisements used to influence readers. What can you conclude about how the ads influenced the students you surveyed?

> **INVESTIGATE FURTHER!**
>
> **TAKE ACTION**
>
> Survey at least ten adults, using the same survey questions. Create charts to display your results. Then compare the adults' responses with the students' responses. How do the results compare? What can you conclude?

Investigate Further

Take Action

Survey results may vary depending upon the community. You might want students to compare their results with those of their classmates. Students should tally the results in their *Science Notebooks* on p. 382.

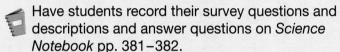 **What conclusions could you make about adults' awareness of the harmful effects of drugs? What conclusions could you make about students' awareness?** Students may find that adult attitudes are very different from student attitudes. Adults may be more aware of the dangers of drug misuse and the dangerous side effects of "recreational" drugs, such as tobacco or alcohol.

Materials Hints You might inquire at a doctor's or dentist's office for discarded magazines.

2. Guide the Procedure

- Suggest that students brainstorm topics for survey questions. Questions might include: Are most medicines helpful? How does tobacco use affect a person's health? At what age should people be allowed to purchase tobacco and alcohol?

- Encourage students to find ads for a variety of drugs that use different strategies of persuasion. Direct them to look for different settings and words in the ads.

- **Why do the ads vary according to their audience?** Students should recognize that ads want the reader to "identify" with the people in them. Ads in men's magazines, for example, show rugged men smoking outdoors. Ads in fashion magazines show young, good-looking people.

Have students record their survey questions and descriptions and answer questions on *Science Notebook* pp. 381–382.

You may wish to have students use the CD-ROM Spreadsheet and Painter to organize and display their data.

3. Assess Performance

Process Skills Checklist

- Did students make charts to **communicate** the results of the surveys they conducted? Did the charts show other students' attitudes about drugs before and after they **observed** magazine ads?

- Did students **infer** that ads try to influence people to use drugs by using pictures and words to make drug use seem appealing?

Analyze and Conclude

1. Students may discover that some students they interview may not consider alcohol and tobacco to be drugs and may not realize that common medicines can be abused, while others may feel the use of drugs should be restricted to medicinal uses.

2. Students may find that the messages in the ads influenced the results of the second survey, making the respondents view drugs more favorably.

3. Students may find that ads try to make drug use seem like a smart or cool thing to do. They may find that the models and settings in the ads try to make drug use appealing. The ads for medicines may suggest that these drugs contribute to better health or make you feel better.

The Misuse of Drugs

Preview *Students focus on different classes of drugs, particularly those that are often abused, and on their effects on the mind and on the body.*

1. Get Ready

Science Terms
drug, caffeine, alcohol, nicotine, illegal drug, substance abuse, addiction

Background

- Generally, the term *drug* is used when referring to illegal or misused drugs, while *medicine* is the term used to refer to over-the-counter and prescription drugs.

- Heroin addicts inject the drug into their bodies with needles. Sometimes these needles have been used before by other addicts. This practice is one way the disease AIDS is spread.

- In addition to health dangers, drug abuse is associated with an increased likelihood of either committing or being the victim of a crime. It is also associated with high suicide rates. Drug abusers are 15 times more likely to commit suicide than are members of the general population. Among young people, drug abuse can prevent proper physical growth, interfere with the development of the brain and nervous system, as well as contribute to a host of family, school, work, and relationship problems.

Discussion Starter

- **What is a drug?** Students may associate the word *drug* only with illegal drugs. Encourage them to try to define the word in a way that will include all kinds of drugs, including medicines.

- **What are some common drugs?** Again, students may name only illegal drugs, such as marijuana. If they do, ask them to think of prescription medicines their doctors sometimes give them or their family. Students may then name drugs such as penicillin, aspirin, cough syrup, and other over-the-counter drugs. They may be surprised to learn that caffeine, alcohol, and tobacco are drugs.

The Misuse of Drugs

Drugs are a common part of our lives. When you are sick, you hope that taking a drug will provide a cure—or at least give some relief. But drugs can also be misused. And when they are misused, they can be very dangerous—even life threatening.

Drugs and Drug Abuse

A **drug** is a substance that can affect the function of body cells and tissues. The kinds of drugs that people can buy in stores are called over-the-counter medicines. To obtain certain types of medical drugs, you need permission from a doctor. Those drugs are called prescription medicines.

Of course, it is very important that you be extremely careful with all drugs. You should not take *any* type of drug—either over-the-counter or prescribed—unless it is given to you by a doctor or by another adult whom you trust. Don't *ever* take even a small amount of a drug on your own.

Certain drugs are found in products that some people use every day. **Caffeine** (ka fēn′) is a drug found in coffee, some teas, chocolate, and some soft drinks. **Alcohol** is a drug found in beer, wine, and other, similar beverages.

Nicotine (nik′ə tēn) is a drug found in tobacco products, such as cigarettes, chewing tobacco, and snuff. Alcohol and nicotine are legal for adults, although their use is regulated.

Finally, there is a whole group of drugs classified as **illegal drugs**. The use of any of these drugs by a person of any age is against the law at all times.

The misuse of any drug is called **substance abuse**. Because drugs affect the function of the body's cells and tissues, the abuse of *any* drug is dangerous.

▲ **Caffeine is found in many familiar food products.**

G50

Integrating the Curriculum

Science & Math

STATISTICS

What You Need resource books; graph paper or Activity Support Master "Graph Paper" (TRB p. 67)

What to Do A great deal of information is now available on the effects of cigarette smoking. Students can research statistics on how people are affected by smoking and by inhaling second-hand smoke. Ask students to make graphs that show the statistical information they find.

What's the Result? Students should display their graphs and explain what they show.

Multi-Age Classroom Students can work in small groups and divide responsibilities according to interest and ability. Some students might look for information and statistics, while others work on the graphs. The group should collaborate on how to put together their presentation.

Alcohol and Tobacco

In our society, adults can legally drink alcoholic beverages and use tobacco products. It is *not* legal for young people to ever use these substances. Drinking alcohol in moderate amounts is generally considered to be "socially acceptable" by some people. But when drinking is done to excess, alcohol can cause tremendous problems. You will look closely at alcohol abuse later in this chapter.

Using tobacco is also considered "socially acceptable," but it has become less so in recent years. To many people, smoking cigarettes, cigars, or pipes seems dirty and annoying. Smoking is also extremely unhealthy.

Smoking is a factor in the deaths of over 400,000 Americans every year. It is the major cause of lung cancer and contributes to heart disease. Even when tobacco is chewed rather than smoked, it can cause disease. Cancers of the mouth and throat are related to the use of chewing tobacco and snuff.

If tobacco is so bad, why do so many people use it? Nicotine, the drug found in tobacco, causes an addiction. An **addiction** is a condition in which a person has extreme difficulty in stop-

ping the use of a drug. The addicted person feels powerless to stop because of the physical or mental problems that would result. Many drugs besides nicotine are addictive.

Most adults who smoke began smoking at a young age, usually as teenagers. In most places it is now illegal to sell tobacco products to children and young teenagers. Although many smokers have been able to quit smoking, many more have been unsuccessful, even with help. Don't let yourself be fooled into starting smoking.

UNIT PROJECT LINK

You've read that the use of drugs affects the function of body cells and tissues. The misuse of drugs can impair the body's coordination. With your group, think of an activity, such as a three-legged race, that demonstrates such impaired coordination. The activity should be safe and easy to do. Make up an advertising slogan about your activity. Warn others of the effect of losing physical control due to the misuse of drugs.

G51

Investigate Further

Unit Project Link

Challenge groups to each think of a competitive physical activity that demonstrates impaired coordination similar to how the body can be affected by the misuse of drugs. Activities exhibiting impaired coordination might include hopping on one leg, writing with your less dominant hand, walking across an open space while blindfolded, and so on. Students' advertising slogans should relate the impaired coordination to possible effects of drug misuse, warning others of the effect of losing physical control. Have students use p. 383 of their *Science Notebooks* and Unit Project Master G5 (TRB p. 112).

2. Guide the Discussion

Choose from the following strategies to facilitate discussion.

Connecting to the Activities

- **Ad Power, pp. G48–G49**
  Look over the ads that you analyzed in the activity. How many are advertising over-the-counter drugs? How many are advertising prescription drugs? Which drugs are advertised most often? Students should find that over-the-counter drugs are the medicinal drugs most often advertised in magazines. Prescription medicines are advertised in publications aimed at consumers and at doctors. Ads for cold remedies, alcohol, and tobacco may appear more often.

- **What do the texts of the ads say? Look at the wording carefully. Do the ads sound factual or do they talk about the product in a general way?** Students should conclude that the texts of ads usually do not make any direct claims, but are slogans designed to make readers associate the product with something desirable. Advertisers are not allowed to lie about their products, but they do not usually offer much, if any, factual data either.

Thinking Critically

- **How might a person misuse an over-the-counter medicine?** A person might use too much of the medicine or might use the medicine too often.

- **What steps can a person take to avoid misusing an over-the-counter medicine?** Read and follow the package directions carefully. Remind students that they should not take *any* medications unless administered by a trusted adult.

Drawing Conclusions

- **Why do you think it is illegal for young people to use alcohol and tobacco?** Students might say that these drugs have a stronger effect on young people than on adults, young people are not mature enough to make a decision to use these drugs, using alcohol can lead to dangerous behaviors, and so on.

Making Comparisons

- **Which drug types increase the activity of the nervous system? Which have the opposite effect?** Stimulants and inhalants stimulate the nervous system, while depressants and narcotics decrease and depress the functions of the brain and nervous system.

- **How are morphine and alcohol similar?** Both depress the activity of the nervous system. Both can damage the liver and other organs and diminish mental capacity.

Connecting to the Activities

- ***Ad Power, pp. G48–G49***
  What information would you put into a public-service ad to convince young people not to take drugs? Explain to students that public-service ads are ads that do not try to sell a product but try to teach people to follow behaviors that will keep them healthier. Suggest that students design public-service ads for radio, television, magazines, or newspapers that might help people understand why they should not drink alcohol, smoke cigarettes, or misuse other drugs. The students might want to aim their ads at specific age groups or at people with such special interests as sports.

Identifying and Solving Problems

What would you say to someone who tried to convince you to drink alcohol or take other drugs? Let volunteers discuss how they would refuse harmful drugs. Responses will probably depend on how the question is posed or the specific situations students envision. If students are uncomfortable with this topic, you might lead a more general discussion on how to resist peer pressure.

DRUGS AND THEIR EFFECTS

Drug Type	Action	Example	Effects of Abuse
Stimulants	Increases activity of the nervous system	Nicotine	Lung disease; damage to heart, throat
		Amphetamines	Extreme nervousness; damage to nervous system; mental capacity diminished
		Cocaine, crack*	Heart attack; damage to nervous system; damage to lining of nose; death from overdose
Depressants	Decreases activity of the nervous system	Barbiturates, methaqualone*, tranquilizers	Damage to nervous system; tiredness; slurred speech; depression; convulsions; death from overdose
		Alcohol	Damage to nervous system, liver, and other organs; mental capacity diminished
Hallucinogens	Alters perception and awareness	Marijuana*, hashish*, LSD*	Lung disease; damage to nervous system; panic; distorted reality; personality changes; mental capacity diminished
Narcotics	Depresses the functions of the brain and nervous system	Morphine, heroin*	Damage to nervous system, liver, and other organs; heart attack; lung disease; personality changes; mental capacity diminished; death from overdose
Inhalants	Increases activity of the nervous system	Glues, paints, aerosol sprays, nitrous oxide	Damage to brain, lungs, liver, bones, kidneys, and nervous system; possible death
Steroids	Increases body mass and strength	Dianabol, Anavar, Winstrol-V	Damage to heart, liver, brain, bones; personality changes; death from overdose

*an illegal drug

G52

Integrating the Curriculum

Science & Social Studies

INTERVIEWING **What You Need** yellow pages of local telephone book

What to Do Some caregivers specialize in helping other people overcome addictions. Students can look in the yellow pages of a telephone book to find the names of places where people who are addicted to drugs can go for help. Suggest that students write letters to these establishments to find out how workers there help people overcome addictions. Students might ask about the workers' approach and about their successes and failures in helping people.

What's the Result? Students can share their findings by telling classmates what they learned and what was the most interesting or surprising thing they discovered.

Illegal Drugs

As you know, drugs affect the body's cells and tissues. The short-term effects of many drugs might seem good to the user. Drugs can relax, excite, or give energy. People take illegal drugs to experience these effects.

But illegal drugs have been made illegal because they also have bad effects. Many drugs are extremely addictive. And most, when used for even a short time, can damage vital body organs, such as the liver, brain, and heart. People who abuse illegal drugs are ignoring the long-term harm simply to get short-term pleasure.

Some illegal drugs are taken by using a needle to inject the drug into the bloodstream. There are many risks associated with injections involving unclean needles. AIDS—a fatal disease of the body's immune system—can be spread by improper use of needles.

Taking illegal drugs involves more than just a health risk. People are arrested and jailed for using illegal drugs. If you think about all that you could lose by using illegal drugs, you won't even be tempted for a minute.

Avoiding Drug Abuse

At some point you may be offered some kind of drug to use. First, you should know exactly what is being offered. Study the table of Drugs and Their Effects on page G52 to gain an understanding of the different kinds of drugs that people use and abuse.

Second, think about the reasons *not* to use drugs. Consider both the health risks and the legal risks.

Third, decide now what you would say if someone offered you an illegal drug or suggested you misuse a legal product. You could simply say, "That's trouble, and I don't want any part of it!" ■

▲ People can learn to overcome their addiction to drugs at treatment centers such as this.

INVESTIGATE FURTHER!

TAKE ACTION

For one week, go through newspapers to find articles on drug abuse. Also find articles that in some way relate to drug abuse, such as drug-related crimes. Discuss your findings with the class.

G53

Investigate Further

Take Action

Students can paste their clippings onto p. 384 of their *Science Notebooks* and include a note of any new ideas or insights they had during the class discussion. Students may see patterns in the articles such as how drug abuse leads to theft to support a drug habit and how violence can result from drug use and the sale of illegal drugs. **What conclusions can you draw about the size and nature of the drug problem in America?** Students might respond that a large number of people may be addicted to illegal drugs; that drug addicts come from all walks of life; that some people make a lot of money from illegal drugs; that police and government have not been successful in stopping drug abuse.

Making Judgments

Why have lawmakers made some drugs illegal? Students might recognize that in addition to the effects these drugs can have on a person's health, they can also affect behavior. In the long term, people who take drugs can become careless about health and work habits. Some even turn to crime in order to get enough money to pay for the drugs they crave.

Thinking Critically

Do you think drug abuse is a problem for only the individual abuser, for his or her family and friends, or for the whole society? Students may respond that drug abuse affects society because of increase in violent crime and money spent to fight drug-related crime.

Responding to Individual Needs

Inclusion Activity Write out the following terms, each at the top of a column on the chalkboard: *over-the-counter medicines, prescription medicines, addictive drugs*. Tell students to review the collection of magazine ads from the activity and to divide the ads into the categories that match the terms on the chalkboard. Have them group the ads on the chalk tray below the appropriate terms.

3. Assess Understanding

As a class, review the following categories: *drugs, medicine, not medicine, over-the-counter, prescription, addictive drugs, legal drugs, and illegal drugs*. Draw a branching chart on the chalkboard starting with the term *drugs* at the top. Ask students to suggest ways to break down the term *drugs* into different categories and to break those categories in turn into subcategories. For example, *drugs* breaks down into *medicine* and *not medicine*; *medicine* breaks down into *over-the-counter* and *prescription*; *not medicine* breaks down into *legal drugs* and *illegal drugs*. Both the legal and illegal drug categories include addictive drugs.

Drugs and Sports

Preview *Students focus on the drugs taken by some athletes and how these drugs affect the body.*

1. Get Ready

Science Terms steroid, stimulant, narcotic

Background

- Companies often use drug testing to check employees and job applicants. A preliminary test, the Rapid Eye Test, can be used by officials when drug abuse is suspected. It checks contraction of the pupil when light is shone into the eye. This reflex does not work well in people taking certain drugs.

Discussion Starter

- **Why might some athletes take or not take illegal drugs?** Some athletes might take such drugs because they want to win at any cost. Others might feel taking drugs is so dishonorable or dangerous that they would not want to do so.

2. Guide the Discussion

Choose from the following strategies to facilitate discussion.

Connecting to the Activities

- *Ad Power, pp. G48–G49*
Why might athletic people be shown in ads?
Consumers might associate the advertised product with looking fit and athletic, which is desirable.

Responding to Individual Needs

Linguistic Activity Students can find articles about the 1988 Summer Olympics and write a paragraph retelling Ben Johnson's story in their own words.

3. Assess Understanding

 Students can list drugs athletes might take to affect performance and explain what the drugs do, why an athlete might take them, and how they are harmful to the body.

Drugs and Sports

 At the sound of the gun, the runners exploded from the starting blocks. This was the 100-meter dash at the 1988 Summer Olympics in Seoul, South Korea. The winner of the race would be called the fastest human alive.

No one who saw the event will ever forget the scene. The sprinters ran in a pack for about half the distance. Then Canada's Ben Johnson seemed to take off like a jet. He crossed the finish line in a burst of speed as the excited crowd cheered its new hero.

But within a few days, Johnson's prized gold medal had been taken back, and his name had been erased forever from the record books. Medical tests showed that Johnson had taken certain drugs to build up his muscles and make himself run faster.

Why Athletes Use Drugs

Athletes feel great pressure to perform. They want to make the first team or win the big race. They know the coach is counting on them. They want to impress their families and friends. Also, winning often means big money.

For those reasons, some athletes try to improve their performances by using drugs. These drugs might help in building muscles, or they might take away the pain of an injury. They might even help the athlete run faster or run longer.

The pressure to use steroids is greatest in sports where strength makes a big difference, such as weight lifting and football. ▼

G54

Investigate Further

Science, Technology & Society

DRUG TESTING

What to Do Drug testing is becoming more common. Athletic organizations and employers use this method to screen for drug use. Opponents say it violates people's rights to privacy. Students can choose which side of the argument they favor and write an essay explaining their views.

Suggest students use the CD-ROM Writer to compose their essays.

What's the Result? Students who favor the same side of the argument could debate students with the opposing view.

Multi-Age Classroom Students could brainstorm ideas and collaborate on their strategy for the debate.

Kinds of Drugs Used

Athletes who abuse drugs mainly use three kinds of drugs—stimulants, narcotics, and steroids. **Steroids** (stir'-oidz) are drugs that act like certain natural chemicals found in the body called hormones. Steroids can help an athlete build up muscles and gain strength. This is the kind of drug that Ben Johnson took. He did get short-term benefits, but he also put himself at risk for long-term damage. The use of steroids can harm the heart and other organs as well as cause personality changes and possible death.

Athletes also use **stimulants**, which speed up the nervous system. A stimulant may make an athlete more active and alert. But abuse over a long period can damage the nervous system.

Finally, athletes with injuries may be tempted to use **narcotics**—heroin, for example. Narcotics can lessen pain, but they're also very addictive. And they can damage many body systems.

Banned From Sports

Athletic organizations forbid the use of steroids, stimulants, and narcotics for two reasons. First, the drugs can be

▲ Although Ben Johnson was the greatest sprinter in Canadian history, his use of steroids cost him an Olympic gold medal.

very harmful to those who take them. And second, they give an unfair advantage to those who use the drugs over those who don't. Ben Johnson cheated, and for that reason he lost his medal.

Sports organizations test athletes for drugs, usually just after a performance or event. A person caught using drugs may be banned from the sport.

Most athletes don't use drugs. With hard work, a good diet, and proper rest, they are able to win fairly and without risking their health. ■

INVESTIGATION 1

1. A friend has just asked you to help her convince young people not to smoke. How would you try to encourage your classmates to avoid tobacco?

2. Explain the difference between the short-term and the long-term effects of drugs. Why should you consider the long-term effects over the short-term effects if you're ever tempted to try drugs?

Assessment

Portfolio

Write a Newspaper Article

Have students pretend it is the day that Olympic doctors tested Ben Johnson and discovered he had used steroids. Invite them to write a front-page headline and news story that tells what happened and why. As a model, you might share with students periodicals, such as *Sports Illustrated*, that reported on the seriousness of the incident.

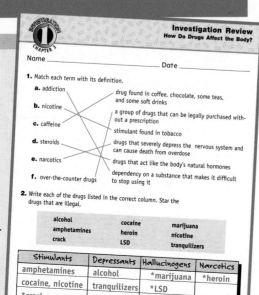

Investigation Review
How Do Drugs Affect the Body?

Name _____ Date _____

1. Match each term with its definition.

a. addiction — drug found in coffee, chocolate, some teas, and some soft drinks

b. nicotine — a group of drugs that can be legally purchased without a prescription

c. caffeine — stimulant found in tobacco

d. steroids — drugs that severely depress the nervous system and can cause death from overdose

e. narcotics — drugs that act like the body's natural hormones

f. over-the-counter drugs — dependency on a substance that makes it difficult to stop using it

2. Write each of the drugs listed in the correct column. Star the drugs that are illegal.

alcohol	cocaine	marijuana
amphetamines	heroin	nicotine
crack	LSD	tranquilizers

Stimulants	Depressants	Hallucinogens	Narcotics
amphetamines	alcohol	*marijuana	*heroin
cocaine, nicotine	tranquilizers	*LSD	
*crack			

Answers should reflect accurate information in a creative way. Any mixture not designed for medical use as an inhalant may contain compounds that can be poisonous.
Process Skills
Communicating
Some paints, glues, office products, and cleansers contain toxins that can be harmful if inhaled. One such use of these substances can cause liver, kidney, or brain damage. On a separate sheet of paper, design an advertisement about the dangers of inhalants.

Critical Thinking Skills
Analyzing, Applying, Generating Ideas, Expressing Ideas

1. Students' responses should include that smoking causes serious damage to health, tobacco is addictive, buying tobacco products is illegal for young people in most places, smoking hurts others nearby, and it is unattractive and messy. Students may choose to use health statistics as well as arguments involving peer pressure.

2. Student responses might indicate that short-term effects can change the way you feel, but long-term effects include addiction and serious damage to health. The long-term effects are so serious they outweigh any possible short-term pleasure.

Challenge The 20th century has produced many advances in medicine, including the invention of many life-saving drugs. Students can investigate some of these drugs and share their findings briefly with the class. You might provide research materials for students to use. They should focus on what the drug is, what problem it treats, and what would happen to patients who didn't have access to it. Remind students that drugs can be beneficial to health but must be used responsibly.

Following Up

Baseline Assessment Return to students' lists of drugs and see if students wish to add any. Were students surprised that certain substances, such as caffeine, or certain categories of substances, such as over-the-counter cold medicines, were drugs?

Reteaching Brainstorm with students to produce a list of 15 to 20 drugs. Together create a Venn diagram classifying the drugs according to the categories you decide on as a group. You may wish to use Activity Support Master "Compare-Contrast Diagram" (TRB p. 68).

Use *Science Notebook* p. 385.

◀ **Investigation Review**
Use Investigation Review p. 170 in the *Assessment Guide*.

HOW DOES ALCOHOL AFFECT THE BODY?

Planner

Subconcept Alcohol has harmful short- and long-term effects on the body and is responsible for many accidents and deaths.

Objectives

- **Investigate** alcohol's short- and long-term effects on the body.
- **Describe** the effects of alcohol on a person's driving ability.

Pacing 1–2 class periods

Science Terms alcoholism, blood alcohol concentration (BAC)

Activate Prior Knowledge

Baseline Assessment Have students work in groups to compile a list that identifies ways in which people may behave when they've been drinking alcohol. Save lists for use in Following Up.

Activity
Alcohol Advertising: Pro and Con

Preview *Students focus on the arguments that can be made both for and against advertisements for alcohol and should realize that there are arguments to be made on both sides.*

Advance Preparation *See p. G46b.*

1. Get Ready

Time about 45 minutes

Grouping 2 teams, each comprising half the class

HOW DOES ALCOHOL AFFECT THE BODY?

When a person takes a drink of alcohol, it goes into the bloodstream almost immediately. Within a few minutes, the alcohol causes changes in the way the person feels and acts. Find out more about the effects of alcohol in Investigation 2.

MATERIALS
- reference materials
- *Science Notebook*

Activity
Alcohol Advertising: Pro and Con

Billboards, magazines, and newspapers all show ads for alcohol, even though it is a drug. What's your stand on whether these ads should be allowed?

Procedure

1. Your teacher will divide your class into teams for a debate. Your team will be either for or against alcohol advertising.

2. **Discuss** your side of the debate with your team members. Divide research responsibilities among members.

3. Use reference materials to find information to support your side of the debate. Also **talk** to people who might give you helpful information. **Record** your information in your *Science Notebook*.

G56

Responding to Individual Needs

Students Acquiring English To reinforce the way an argument can be structured, provide students with boilerplate sentences and ask them to finish the sentences. They may complete the sentences either orally in pairs or in writing, depending on their language needs. Use sentence starters such as:

Alcohol advertising should be banned because... Alcohol advertising should not be banned because...

4. Talk with your team members and share information. Decide on your strongest points. **Predict** what points the other side will make. Plan your arguments.

5. Debate the other team. Your teacher will act as a moderator.

Analyze and Conclude

1. What were the strongest points your team made? What arguments against these points did the other team use?

2. What were the strongest points made by the other team? What arguments against these points did your team members use?

3. Which team do you think won the debate? Explain.

Step 5

G57

Investigate Further

Take Action

The letters students write should express an opinion and back it up with some of the arguments used in the debate. Students should outline their letters on p. 387 of their *Science Notebooks*. You might want to send student letters to a newspaper in the school or community. **Why do you think the points you included in your letter were the best points made in the debate? What other points might you add, now that you have heard the whole debate? How can you verify the points that you made in your letter?** Students might indicate that they can verify their points by doing more research and finding more statistics on the topic.

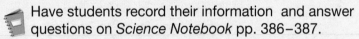

INVESTIGATE FURTHER!

TAKE ACTION

Use the best points from your debate to write a letter to an editor of a newspaper or magazine. Explain how you feel about the issue of alcohol advertising.

Multi-Age Strategy Divide the class into groups of about equal abilities to review resource materials. Let them do as much as they are capable of and share information they gather. Each group should choose one or two strong speakers to present the material and lead the debate.

Materials Hints To finish the activity in one class period, provide resources on several levels of difficulty that clearly state arguments for or against alcohol advertising.

2. Guide the Procedure

Prompt students as they work, using the following questions: **What arguments are the authors making? How can you organize the arguments to make the strongest case for your team?**

• Before groups begin research responsibilities, help them to divide topics or materials.

• Suggest that students list predictions of points the other side might make and try to answer each.

Have students record their information and answer questions on *Science Notebook* pp. 386–387.

You may wish to have students use the CD-ROM Spreadsheet to organize and display their data.

3. Assess Performance

Process Skills Checklist

• Did students **record data** that supported positions for and against alcohol advertising? Was their data **collected** from reference materials?

• Did students accurately **predict** what arguments the opposing team would make? Did they plan their own arguments based on these predictions?

Analyze and Conclude

1-2. The strongest argument for advertising might be that it is a right to free speech. Other arguments for advertising might include that doubt exists about a direct relationship between ads and alcohol abuse. People have a choice to drink and it's up to them to believe the ads or not. The strongest argument made against advertising might be that advertising leads to destructive behavior. Other arguments against advertising might include that it is not a right or that the need to protect health outweighs the right.

3. Winners should be determined by the strength of the arguments and the skill of the debaters; however, fifth-graders are likely to feel that arguments against ads outweigh arguments for ads.

Alcohol in the Body

Preview *Students focus on the short- and long-term effects of alcohol on the body and find out how they can be damaging.*

1. Get Ready

Science Terms alcoholism

Background

- For both genetic and environmental reasons, children of alcoholics are among those at highest risk for becoming problem drinkers themselves. There are an estimated seven million children of alcoholics in America. Other children at risk include those whose lives are stressful for other reasons, such as being a scapegoat at school, having a learning disability, or coming from a dysfunctional family.

Discussion Starter

 Since alcohol interferes with the functions of the nervous system, how do you think people who are drinking alcohol probably behave? Think about what you learned in the last chapter about the role the nervous system plays in the body. Based on their previous knowledge, students may predict that drinkers' senses are dulled or reduced. They may suggest that messages from the brain do not reach the muscles properly, causing slowed or unsteady movements.

What do you think are some of the long-term health effects of alcohol use? Encourage speculation about these effects. Students probably will not know about damage to organs, but they might speculate about damage to the brain, digestive system, and nervous system.

Alcohol in the Body

Have you ever seen adults who have been drinking beer or wine? They can seem pretty silly, with a little too much laughter and loud talking.

Actually, people may drink alcoholic beverages just to get those kinds of effects. Sometimes, alcohol can seem to lift a person's spirits. Shyness falls away, and it seems easier to relax.

The problem is that alcohol can be very dangerous to the body, especially when abused. You may decide you want to drink when you become an adult. But before you do, you should learn what alcohol does to the body.

What Happens to the Body

Alcohol is a part of every alcoholic beverage, including beer, wine, and the various liquors. When a person drinks one of these beverages, the alcohol in the drink is absorbed directly into the bloodstream through the walls of the stomach. Unlike food, alcohol does not need to be digested, and so it quickly moves throughout the body.

In the body, alcohol increases both the heart rate and the blood pressure. The blood vessels in the skin expand. That effect often results in a reddishness of the drinker's nose and cheeks. Sometimes people think the drinker

G58

looks warm, and maybe the face is. But alcohol actually causes a loss of heat from the body. No one should ever drink alcohol to keep warm.

Another misunderstanding is that drinking alcohol adds fluids to the body. Actually, alcohol causes the tissues of the body to lose water. So despite drinking even a large amount of alcohol, a person could end up with less fluid than his or her body needs.

Alcohol is a depressant drug. It depresses the workings of the nervous system. It affects how well the brain functions and how well the neurons throughout the body carry messages.

This effect on the nervous system is what causes people to become less shy, for example. But the effect also accounts for many of the dangers of drinking alcohol. Physically, people become slow and clumsy. All kinds of accidents can result. Also, thinking is affected. Bad judgment can lead to accidents as well as to lost friendships and missed opportunities.

A Drinker's Fate

Bad things can happen to a person in just a few hours of drinking. A person who has been drinking is more likely than others to cause accidents.

Integrating the Curriculum

Science & Language Arts

WRITE A STORY **What to Do** Draw two columns on the chalkboard. In the first column, write from top to bottom: 1 drink, 2 drinks, 3 drinks, 4 drinks, 5 drinks. In the second, aligned with items in the first column from top to bottom, write: slight effect; control of muscles slightly impaired; reaction time slows/judgment impaired; coordination and memory greatly affected; limited awareness of surroundings. Ask students to write a short story in which a person drinks a given amount of alcohol and then tries to perform a mental or physical activity, such as studying, riding a bicycle, singing, or playing a sport.

What's the Result? **Do the stories fit the information on the chalkboard?** The number of drinks consumed by people in the story should produce the effects shown for that number of drinks.

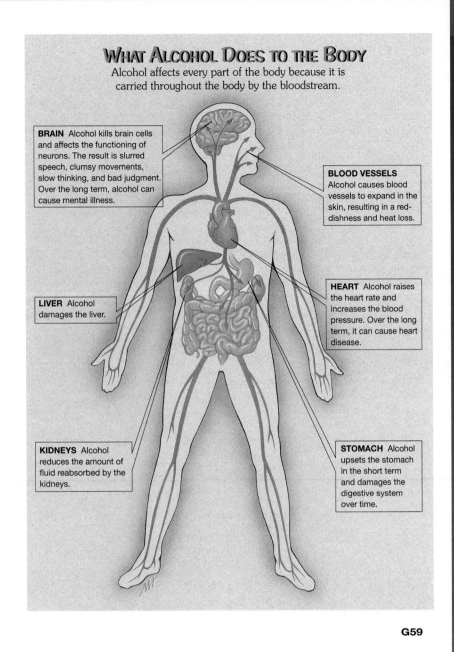

WHAT ALCOHOL DOES TO THE BODY

Alcohol affects every part of the body because it is carried throughout the body by the bloodstream.

BRAIN Alcohol kills brain cells and affects the functioning of neurons. The result is slurred speech, clumsy movements, slow thinking, and bad judgment. Over the long term, alcohol can cause mental illness.

BLOOD VESSELS Alcohol causes blood vessels to expand in the skin, resulting in a reddishness and heat loss.

LIVER Alcohol damages the liver.

HEART Alcohol raises the heart rate and increases the blood pressure. Over the long term, it can cause heart disease.

KIDNEYS Alcohol reduces the amount of fluid reabsorbed by the kidneys.

STOMACH Alcohol upsets the stomach in the short term and damages the digestive system over time.

G59

Investigate Further

Cultural Connection

DISCUSS IDEAS **What to Do** Suggest that students work in groups to discuss how attitudes toward drinking might change people's drinking habits. Explain that in some countries, including China, Italy, and Israel, drinking alcohol is a normal part of everyday life. Drinking in moderation is not forbidden, but drunkenness is strongly disapproved of. These countries have substantially lower rates of alcoholism. Have each student group develop a plan of action that might help lower the rate of alcoholism in this country.

What's the Result? Students will probably recognize that peer pressure and societal attitudes toward drinking can change people's drinking habits.

Multi-Age Classroom Students should consult on which ideas to include in the plans, with all students contributing ideas.

2. Guide the Discussion

Choose from the following strategies to facilitate discussion.

Connecting to the Activities

- *Alcohol Advertising: Pro and Con, pp. G56–G57.* **What were some of the arguments made in favor of banning advertising? What information in this resource could be used to back up these arguments?** Information about the immediate dangers of drunkenness and the damaging effects of long-term alcohol abuse could be used to back up the arguments.

Drawing Conclusions

- **Why do you think that in our society people often forget that alcohol is a drug?** Probably because alcohol is legal and considered "socially acceptable" by some people. **How do you know that alcohol is really a drug?** Like other drugs, alcohol causes changes in the way the body functions, and like many other drugs, it can be harmful and addictive.

Making Comparisons

- **On which body system is the effect of alcohol most visible? Explain.** Alcohol most visibly affects the nervous system, causing a person to show changed behavior and physical coordination shortly after drinking.

Making Inferences

Alcohol causes blood vessels in the skin to expand. How does this cause the body to lose heat? The expanded blood vessels carry more blood to the skin. As a result, more heat from the blood moves to the surrounding air.

How can drinking alcohol lead to increased urination? Alcohol reduces the amount of water reabsorbed by the kidneys. Thus, more water reaches the bladder and is eventually released.

Responding to Individual Needs

Students Acquiring English On the chalkboard, list in English: *red cheeks, liver disease, clumsiness, mental illness, heart disease, loss of body heat, loss of body fluid, bad judgment, accidents, lost friendships,* and *digestive problems.* Have students translate these effects of drinking alcohol into their native language. Write the translations next to the English versions.

Drawing Conclusions

- **How can nondrinkers sometimes be affected by other people's drinking?** Students may give examples that include unborn babies whose mothers drink, drivers involved in car accidents with drunk drivers, and family members of alcoholics.

Responding to Individual Needs

Gifted and Talented Activity Students might be interested in researching and reporting on support groups for alcoholics and their families, such as Alcoholics Anonymous (AA), Al-anon, and Alateen. Reports should include how the support groups can be contacted, how they are organized and structured, and how they help alcoholics and their families.

SCIENCE IN LITERATURE

Native American Doctor:
The Story of Susan LaFlesche Picotte
by Jeri Ferris

Suggest that students write a biographical essay about Susan LaFlesche Picotte. Essays should explain why this doctor saw alcohol abuse as the greatest medical problem of the Native Americans and how she tried to help those who had this problem.

3. Assess Understanding

Students can work in groups of three or four to design posters advertising reasons not to drink. They can draw, write slogans, use magazine clippings, or use any of the CD-ROM graphic tools to create their ads. You might want to display the posters in the classroom or school.

Violent behavior often accompanies drinking too much alcohol. A person who abuses alcohol over many years causes serious damage to the body.

Some people can become addicted to alcohol just as they can become addicted to other drugs. The disease that results is called **alcoholism**. The alcohol addict, or alcoholic, may suffer from many illnesses or disorders.

Alcohol destroys brain cells. The alcoholic gradually loses brain function and may become mentally ill. Alcohol severely damages the liver, and many alcoholics die from liver disease. Over a period of time, alcohol also causes digestive problems and heart disease. There is no question that alcohol has destroyed many lives.

Perhaps more tragic is that alcohol can also affect an unborn child. When a pregnant woman drinks alcohol, the alcohol also enters her baby's system. This can then result in fetal alcohol syndrome, a condition in which the baby is born deformed or with a damaged nervous system.

Avoiding Alcohol Use

Sometimes it might seem like most adults drink alcohol. Actually, only about half do. Many adults have decided that the long-term risks to health are not worth any short-term pleasure.

Certainly it is more risky for young people to drink, because their bodies are still growing. It is also illegal for a person your age to drink alcohol. ∎

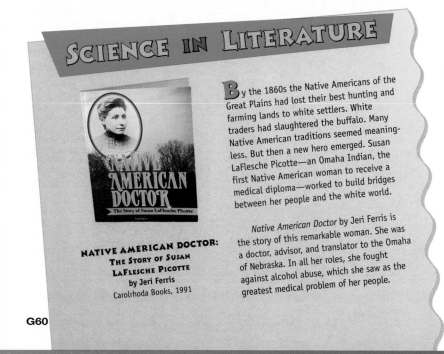

SCIENCE IN LITERATURE

NATIVE AMERICAN DOCTOR:
THE STORY OF SUSAN
LaFLESCHE PICOTTE
by Jeri Ferris
Carolrhoda Books, 1991

By the 1860s the Native Americans of the Great Plains had lost their best hunting and farming lands to white settlers. White traders had slaughtered the buffalo. Many Native American traditions seemed meaningless. But then a new hero emerged. Susan LaFlesche Picotte—an Omaha Indian, the first Native American woman to receive a medical diploma—worked to build bridges between her people and the white world.

Native American Doctor by Jeri Ferris is the story of this remarkable woman. She was a doctor, advisor, and translator to the Omaha of Nebraska. In all her roles, she fought against alcohol abuse, which she saw as the greatest medical problem of her people.

G60

Investigate Further

Integrating the Sciences

PHYSICAL SCIENCE

What You Need periodic table

What to Do On the chalkboard write the chemical formulas for methanol (CH_4O), ethanol (C_2H_6O), and isopropyl alcohol (C_3H_8O). Tell students that ethanol is the alcohol found in certain beverages. It is very dilute in a drink; however, in its less diluted forms, it is strong enough to dissolve many other substances. Using a periodic table, have students identify the kinds of atoms that make up alcohols (carbon, hydrogen, and oxygen). They should then compare the numbers of each kind of atom in the three alcohols.

What's the Result? Help students recognize that the three kinds of alcohols show varying numbers of carbon and hydrogen atoms.

Alcohol and Driving

A leading cause of death among teenagers is drunk driving. ▶

The leading cause of death among American teenagers is accidents. Alcohol is a factor in about half of all accidents that are auto-related. It contributes to the deaths of as many as 20,000 people every year.

The high number of auto deaths involving alcohol has caused Americans to take a harsh view of anyone who drinks and then drives. Penalties for such lawbreaking are severe.

Highway Safety

Every state has laws against driving under the influence of alcohol. When

an accident occurs, the police check whether a driver has been drinking by testing the person's **blood alcohol concentration (BAC)**. A BAC test shows how much alcohol is in the person's blood, and that tells how many drinks the person has had.

The table on page G62 shows how a certain number of drinks changes the BAC and affects the drinker. In most states a person is considered legally intoxicated, usually known as being drunk, when the BAC is 0.1 percent or more. But no one should drive after having even one drink, because judgment will have been impaired.

G61

Integrating the Curriculum

Science & Social Studies

GET MADD **What You Need** materials that provide information about MADD and SADD

What to Do Provide information about the organizations MADD (Mothers Against Drunk Driving) and SADD (Students Against Drunk Driving). Review materials with students and discuss what these organizations do to try to put an end to drunk driving. Contact a representative of one of these groups and ask them to make a presentation to your class. Suggest that students write a summary of what they learn.

What's the Result? Students can share their findings with the class and with other classes by giving an oral report, designing a poster, or using some other method of their choice.

Alcohol and Driving

Preview *Students focus on drunk driving as a major cause of auto accidents.*

1. Get Ready

Science Terms blood alcohol concentration (BAC)

Background

- Laws alone have limited effectiveness on drunk driving. Perhaps the most important tactic in prevention is peer pressure. The National Committee Against Drunk Driving says making drunken behavior socially taboo is a cornerstone. Party hosts, businesses that provide alcohol, and workplaces can all play a role in making drunkenness "uncool."

Discussion Starter

How do you predict that alcohol will affect someone's ability to drive? Students might name slow reaction time, poor coordination, and bad judgment as effects on driving ability.

2. Guide the Discussion

Use the following strategy to facilitate discussion.

Connecting to the Activities

- *Alcohol Advertising: Pro and Con, pp. G56–G57.* **Why do you think alcohol companies run ads against drinking and driving?** The companies want people to drink responsibly, they don't want people to associate alcohol with accidents, and they want to appear responsible in the eyes of the public.

3. Assess Understanding

Students can make a collage of magazine photos, words, and drawings to identify the likely outcomes of drunk driving.

Close the Investigation

Critical Thinking Skills
Analyzing, Synthesizing, Applying

WRITE IT **1.** Students should indicate such short-term effects of alcohol as increase in heart rate and blood pressure, expansion of blood vessels in the skin, tissue water loss, depressed and impaired functions of the nervous system, and violent behavior. Long-term effects can include addiction, loss of brain function, liver damage, digestive and heart diseases, and deformed babies. Short-term effects can impact on others if a person whose judgment is impaired by alcohol causes an automobile accident or becomes violent.

2. Since alcohol depresses the activity of the nervous system, drinking alcohol combined with a medication that depresses the nervous system could result in severe damage to the nervous system, or even death.

Challenge Ask students to find out how a breathalyzer test works and explain it to the class. They might contact the local police station for this information. Explain that sometimes when police officers can't do a breathalyzer test, they ask drivers to close their eyes and touch their nose or walk a straight line. Ask students to explain the purpose of this test (assessing coordination).

Following Up

Baseline Assessment Return to the lists students made of people's behavior when they've been drinking. Ask students if they wish to add behaviors to the list.

Reteaching List the following terms on the chalkboard: *circulatory system, muscular system, digestive system, nervous system*, and *excretory system*. Under each term, ask volunteers to describe one way in which alcohol affects that body system.

 Use *Science Notebook* p. 388.

Investigation Review ▶
Use Investigation Review p. 171 in the *Assessment Guide*.

▲ Police may use a BAC-testing device if they suspect a driver has been drinking.

Young People and Drunk Driving

Teenagers who are old enough to drive are just gaining experience at that skill. Imagine adding the effects of illegal alcohol consumption to their inexperience! The result of this combination is that a large number of alcohol-related traffic accidents involve teenagers.

What does this mean for you? Don't *ever* get into a car with anyone who has been drinking. And when you're on a bike or crossing a street, watch carefully for reckless drivers. Stay alert so that you won't become involved in an alcohol-related accident. ■

Drinks in 1 hr	BAC (%)	Effects on a Driver (weight, 120 lb)
1	0.03	Increase in heart rate; decrease in coordination
2	0.05	Reduced ability to make good decisions; reduced coordination
3	0.08	Decrease in attention and alertness; slurred speech; slowness in reactions; further decrease in ability to make good decisions
4	0.10	Legally intoxicated; very slow reaction time; terrible coordination; loss of balance; further decrease in ability to make good decisions
5	0.13	Visibly intoxicated; vomiting; poor body control and decision making
6	0.16	Limited awareness; almost no control of body or decision making

INVESTIGATION 2

1. Describe some of the short-term and long-term effects of alcohol on the body. How are some of the short-term effects dangerous not only to drinkers but also to others around them?

2. Why is a warning to avoid drinking alcohol often shown on medicines that depress the activity of the nervous system?

G62

Assessment

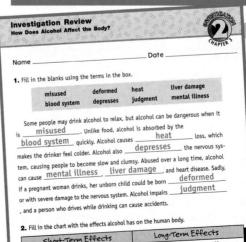

Investigation Review
How Does Alcohol Affect the Body?

Name _____ Date _____

1. Fill in the blanks using the terms in the box.

| misused | deformed | heat | liver damage |
| blood system | depresses | judgment | mental illness |

Some people may drink alcohol to relax, but alcohol can be dangerous when it is __misused__. Unlike food, alcohol is absorbed by the __blood system__ quickly. Alcohol causes __heat__ loss, which makes the drinker feel colder. Alcohol also __depresses__ the nervous system, causing people to become slow and clumsy. Abused over a long time, alcohol can cause __mental illness__, __liver damage__, and heart disease. Sadly, if a pregnant woman drinks, her unborn child could be born __deformed__ or with severe damage to the nervous system. Alcohol impairs __judgment__, and a person who drives while drinking can cause accidents.

2. Fill in the chart with the effects alcohol has on the human body.

Short-Term Effects	Long-Term Effects
expansion of blood vessels causing an increase in heart rate and blood pressure, heat loss and reddish color; impairment of brain functions resulting in slurred speech, clumsy movements, slow thinking, and poor judgement; upset stomach	mental illness, liver disease, heart disease, and digestive system damage

Process Skills
Communicating, Making Decisions
You have just watched a sporting event on television and seen commercials for alcoholic beverages. You've decided to write a letter to the television network about the ads. On a separate sheet of paper list the main points you will make in your letter.

Students' answers should reflect the decision-making and communication skills that they have used in their debates about alcohol advertising.

Performance

Interview Invite a police officer or social worker to class to talk about his or her experiences with alcohol-related problems. Students should be encouraged to develop questions beforehand to ask the guest.

REFLECT & EVALUATE

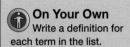

WORD POWER

- addiction
- alcohol
- alcoholism
- blood alcohol concentration
- caffeine
- drug
- illegal drugs
- narcotics
- nicotine
- steroids
- stimulants
- substance abuse

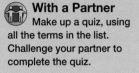 **On Your Own**
Write a definition for each term in the list.

 With a Partner
Make up a quiz, using all the terms in the list. Challenge your partner to complete the quiz.

BUILD YOUR PORTFOLIO

Make a concept map, starting with the word *drug*. On your concept map, include both legal and illegal drugs and some of their effects.

Analyze Information

Study the drawing. Then identify the organs that are affected by alcohol and explain how alcohol reaches those organs.

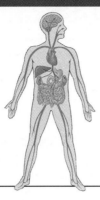

Assess Performance

Design a test to find out how advertisements for drugs influence people. You might want to have people answer questions about various ads or challenge them to match slogans to the correct products, or you may have a different idea. Discuss your findings with your classmates.

Problem Solving

1. Imagine there's a debate over whether to allow members to smoke at your youth center. What arguments could you use to convince others that it's not a good idea to allow smoking?

2. Why might it be harmful for you to take some of another family member's leftover prescription medicine when you have similar symptoms?

3. How could you discourage a friend on your team from using steroids when he or she feels a lot of pressure to succeed in a sport?

4. You've arranged to ride home from a party with a friend. Your friend's sister picks you up, and you haven't gone far before you realize that she's been drinking. What should you do?

G63

Chapter Test pp. 172–173 in the Assessment Guide

Chapter Test Staying in Control

Name _____ Date _____

Analyze Information Each item worth 12 points.

For questions 1–4, circle the letter of the best answer.

1. Which of the following substances is absorbed directly into the bloodstream, depresses the nervous system, and causes long-term liver and heart disease?

a. nicotine
b. any drug
c. alcohol
d. caffeine

2. Which of the following is a fatal disease of the body's immune system that can be spread by improper use of needles?

a. alcoholism
b. AIDS
c. addiction
d. cancer

3. Drugs that act like hormones and can damage the heart and other organs are ___.

a. stimulants
b. narcotics
c. inhalants
d. steroids

4. Marijuana, hashish, and LSD are all kinds of ___, which can alter perception and awareness.

a. stimulants
b. hallucinogens
c. depressants
d. narcotics

Chapter Test Staying in Control

Name _____ Date _____

Problem Solving Each item worth 12 points.

5. Suppose you are at a friend's house and her older brother asks you to try some illegal drugs. What should you do?
Students' answers should include a discussion about the dangers of using drugs as mentioned in the text, as well as how they would refuse the offer to use drugs.

6. Suppose you find out that a friend is using stimulants to be more alert and active at sports. What could you tell your friend to discourage her from using these drugs?
Students' answers should include a discussion about the effects of stimulants on the body, such as how they can damage the nervous system.

Word Power Each item worth 4 points.

_n each blank with a word or phrase from the box.

| stimulants | narcotics | illegal drugs | addiction |

_ condition in which a person has
_xtreme difficulty stopping the use
_ a drug   addiction

_orphine, heroin   narcotics

_otine, amphetamines, cocaine, crack   stimulants

_ijuana, crack, heroin, LSD   illegal drugs

REFLECT & EVALUATE

Word Power

 On Your Own Encourage students to use the Glossary to check their definitions.

 With a Partner Students' clues for terms should reflect an understanding of the terms.

Analyze Information

Alcohol is absorbed directly into the bloodstream from the stomach. It increases both blood pressure and heart rate. Blood carries alcohol to the brain where it affects neuron function and also kills brain cells. Alcohol damages the liver and the digestive system, and it reduces the efficiency of the kidneys.

Assess Performance

Assess students' tests based on advertisements studied and method used to evaluate their influence.

Problem Solving

1. It is illegal for minors to buy tobacco products, it can damage the lungs and heart, and it smells bad.

2. Similar symptoms may not indicate the same illness. The medicine might worsen your condition.

3. Stress that steroids are illegal; they can harm the heart and other organs as well as cause death.

4. You might exit the car so that you can go back and call for a ride, or find a ride with another friend.

 Use *Science Notebook* pp. 389–390.

BUILD YOUR PORTFOLIO

Students' concept maps should include examples of both legal drugs, such as alcohol, and illegal drugs, such as marijuana. You may wish to provide students with a copy of Activity Support Master "Word Web" (TRB p. 70).

UNIT PROJECT:
The Big Event

Students can begin their final preparations for The Bone, Muscle, Brain Triathlon by deciding on a guest list and then designing and making special invitations, perhaps in the form of a ticket for an athletic event. On the day before the event, have students work in groups to prepare and decorate the area where the triathlon events will be held. For example, groups can gather the equipment, set up the props, make a welcoming banner, prepare a refreshments table if you plan to serve snacks, plan for some kind of awards ceremony at the conclusion of the day, and make copies of a program listing the triathlon events and their estimated times to distribute to the guests. Check to see if any students have health conditions that may prevent them from participating. Students who cannot take part in these events can participate by keeping score or judging. For more information on the Big Event, see Wrapping Up the Project p. G1l. For assessment use Unit Project Scoring Rubric Master G6 (TRB p. 113).

 Have students use *Science Notebook* p. 391.

Experiment

Before students begin work on the experiment, have them develop plans to aid in recording their observations. Allow time for students to share their conclusions about the importance of having an opposable thumb with the class.

Research

Before students begin work on their reports, encourage them to develop outlines to organize their research and to assist in their report writing. Set aside an area of the classroom where students can display their reports. You might also wish to invite other classes to come in and hear about the students' findings.

Take Action

In addition to posters, poems, stories, and public-service announcements, invite students to create a program to present to younger students about saying no to drugs. Students can write a script, make costumes, gather props, rehearse, and then take their show from classroom to classroom.

Throughout this unit you've investigated questions related to movement and control. How will you use what you've learned and share that information with others? Here are some ideas.

Hold a Big Event
to Share Your Unit Project

Work with your classmates to plan The Bone, Muscle, Brain Triathlon. This competitive athletic meet will have three categories: Movement Events, Coordination Events, and Impaired Coordination Events. Use the physical activities that your group planned for the Unit Project Links. Gather any props and equipment you may need. Then invite families and friends to come enjoy the Triathlon...and have fun!

Experiment

Explore this test of muscular control. Tape your thumb to the side of your hand. Then use that hand to pick up a pencil. Can you control your fingers well? What adjustments do you have to make? What can you conclude about the importance of having an opposable thumb?

Research

Choose a sport that you enjoy or would like to learn. Find out which muscles must be developed to excel in this sport. Does a baseball player, for example, need to stretch, build upper or lower body strength, or need aerobic exercise? Write and share a report about your sport.

Take Action

Think of a way to educate others about the dangers of tobacco, alcohol, and other drugs. You might write a story or poem, produce radio announcements, design posters, or do something else that will discourage people from using drugs. Carry out your plan yourself or with some classmates.

G64

Home-School Connection

Closing Letter

Dear Family,

We hope that you have enjoyed finding out about how the human body works. Would you like to find out more? Here are some additional activities that you and your student can do together.

• Pick up free information at your local hospital or family health clinic on the dangers of substance abuse. For a free catalog of materials on this subject, send your name and address to: National Clearinghouse for Alcohol and Drug Information, P. O. Box 2345, Rockville, MD 20852. You can also request the catalog by calling 1-800-729-6686. There is no charge for this call.

• Plan some healthful family activities that use bones and muscles, such as hiking, swimming, or bicycling. As you do these activities together, talk about how the body works.

• Read more about it! Here are some books about the human body that you can find at your local library or bookstore.

Exploring Your Skeleton: Funny Bones and Not-So-Funny Bones by Pamela R. Bishop (Watts, 1991). A fun book about the skeletal system written for young readers.

The Body Book by Sara Stein (Workman, 1992). A wide range of facts written in a newsbrief form is accompanied by photographs and organized into sections titled "Stuff," "Guts," and "Senses."

How the Body Works by Steve Parker (Dorling Kindersley, 1994). An extraordinarily well-designed, well-written, and well-illustrated volume is complete with glossary and index.

The Closing Letter at the end of this unit suggests additional activities and books that family members can share at home to investigate how the body works. Distribute the Closing Letter (TRB p. 37) to students at the end of this unit.

MATERIALS LIST

Below is a complete list of materials needed for all activities included in Unit G. Quantities are indicated for a class of 30 students working in groups of 5. Materials included in the Unit Equipment Kit are indicated with a [*].

Materials	Quantity	Activity Page
Consumable Materials		
bone specimens	6	G6
gloves, plastic*	30 pairs	G6
index cards*	180	G34
magazines	variety	G48
markers*	15	G34, G38
paper fasteners*	1 box	G7
paper towels	1 roll	G6
posterboard	30 sheets	G7, G48
tape	classroom	G7, G48
Nonconsumable Materials		
books	15	G26
clips, spring	15	G16
goggles*	30	G6
hand lenses*	6	G6
metersticks*	15	G27
model of human skeleton*	1	G7
reference materials	variety	G56
scissors	15	G7, G48
tape measures*	15	G14
timers*	6	G16, G34

CREDITS

Front Cover: Photography: Jade Albert; Photography Production: Picture It Corporation; Illustration: Deborah Haley Melmon.

TOC: Dom Doyle, Patrick Gnan, Robert Pasternack, Michael Sloan, Elsa Warnick.

Contributing Artists:
Unit 5G Chapter G1: May Cheney: 8, 9, 10, 11; Kathleen Dunne: 8, 19, 20, 21, 22; Jackie Heda: 12, 19, 20; Bob Swanson: 13; Kate Sweeney: 17, 18, 23. **Chapter G2:** Scott Barrows: 30, 31; Eldon Doty: 40, 41; Dom Doyle: 28; Marcia Hartsock: 37, 38, 39, 42, 45; Jackie Heda: 31; Jane Hurd: 31, 32; Robert Margulies: 33; Steve McInturff: 44; Briar Lee Mitchell: 29. **Chapter G3:** Medical Art Co.: 59, 63; Bob Novak: 50, 51, 53; Ray Vella: 52, 61.

Glossary: Lori Anzalone, Patrick Gnan, Carlyn Iverson, Fran Milner, Robert Pasternack.

Handbook: Kathleen Dunne, Laurie Hamilton, Catherine Leary, Andy Meyer.

Teaching Guide Front Matter: Olivia McElroy: Common Art; Patrick Gnan: T6, T7.

Table of Contents: Dom Doyle.

Common Art for Unit Opener pages, Tips from Teacher pages, Technology pages, Chapter Opener pages, Home School Icons, Book Icons, Videotape Icons: Nancy Tobin.

Common Art for Project File pages: Jenny Campbell.

Photographs:
All photographs by Silver Burdett Ginn (SBG) unless otherwise noted.

Unit G Opener 1: *border* Don W. Fawcett/Visuals Unlimited. Chapter 1 4–5: *bkgd.* Steven E. Sutton/Duomo; *l. inset* Michael Amberger/The Stock Market; *r. inset* Focus on Sports. 6–16: Grant Huntington for SBG. 20: *t.* Visuals Unlimited ; *b.* Custom Medical Stock Photo. 21–22: Grant Huntington for SBG. Chapter 2 24–25: *bkgd.* David M. Phillips/Visuals Unlimited; *l. inset* Guy L'Heureux for SBG; *r. inset* Runk/Schoenberger/Grant Heilman Photography. 26–35: Richard Hutchings for SBG. 43: Yoav Levy/Photake. 44: Max Aguilera-Hellweg. Chapter 3 46–47: *bkgd.* SuperStock; *inset* L. Steinmark/Custom Medical Stock Photo. 48–50: Grant Huntington for SBG. 53: Blair Seitz/The PhotoFile. 54: Focus on Sports. 55: David Madison/Duomo. 61: Picture Perfect USA. 62: M. Siluk/The Image Works.

Teaching Guide Front Matter:
T2–T3: © Stephen Dalton/Photo Researchers, Inc. G1e: © John Bavosi/Science Photo Library/Photo Researchers, Inc.

Teacher Notes

TEACHER NOTES

TEACHER NOTES

TEACHER NOTES

Teacher Notes

Teacher Notes

TEACHER NOTES

TEACHER NOTES

TEACHER NOTES

TEACHER NOTES

THINK LIKE A SCIENTIST

You don't have to be a professional scientist to act and think like one. Thinking like a scientist mostly means using common sense. It also means learning how to test your ideas in a careful way.

In other words, *you* can think like a scientist.

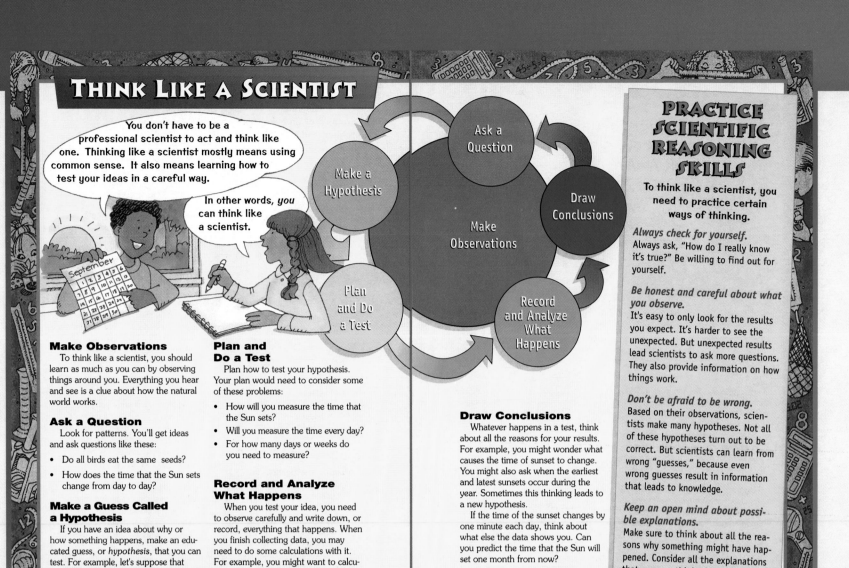

Ask a Question

Make a Hypothesis

Draw Conclusions

Make Observations

Plan and Do a Test

Record and Analyze What Happens

To think like a scientist, you need to practice certain ways of thinking.

Always check for yourself.
Always ask, "How do I really know it's true?" Be willing to find out for yourself.

Be honest and careful about what you observe.
It's easy to only look for the results you expect. It's harder to see the unexpected. But unexpected results lead scientists to ask more questions. They also provide information on how things work.

Don't be afraid to be wrong.
Based on their observations, scientists make many hypotheses. Not all of these hypotheses turn out to be correct. But scientists can learn from wrong "guesses," because even wrong guesses result in information that leads to knowledge.

Keep an open mind about possible explanations.
Make sure to think about all the reasons why something might have happened. Consider all the explanations that you can think of.

Make Observations

To think like a scientist, you should learn as much as you can by observing things around you. Everything you hear and see is a clue about how the natural world works.

Ask a Question

Look for patterns. You'll get ideas and ask questions like these:

- Do all birds eat the same seeds?
- How does the time that the Sun sets change from day to day?

Make a Guess Called a Hypothesis

If you have an idea about why or how something happens, make an educated guess, or *hypothesis*, that you can test. For example, let's suppose that your hypothesis about the sunset time is that it changes by one minute each day.

Plan and Do a Test

Plan how to test your hypothesis. Your plan would need to consider some of these problems:

- How will you measure the time that the Sun sets?
- Will you measure the time every day?
- For how many days or weeks do you need to measure?

Record and Analyze What Happens

When you test your idea, you need to observe carefully and write down, or record, everything that happens. When you finish collecting data, you may need to do some calculations with it. For example, you might want to calculate how much the sunset time changes in a week or a month.

Draw Conclusions

Whatever happens in a test, think about all the reasons for your results. For example, you might wonder what causes the time of sunset to change. You might also ask when the earliest and latest sunsets occur during the year. Sometimes this thinking leads to a new hypothesis.

If the time of the sunset changes by one minute each day, think about what else the data shows you. Can you predict the time that the Sun will set one month from now?

WHAT CAUSES THE ROCK IN STATUES TO WEAR AWAY?

Here's an example of an everyday problem and how thinking like a scientist can help you explore it.

Ask a Question

Make a Hypothesis

Donelle and Ramon were walking through downtown when Ramon pointed to a statue, laughed, and said, "Look, that poor guy's nose has fallen off." Donelle laughed and as they both took a closer look at the statue, they could see that most of the statue's face was missing. Even the statue's body was pitted.

Donelle thought she knew why. She suspected that rain, snow, and ice were destroying the statue. "But it's stone," Ramon argued. "Stone doesn't dissolve in water. Does it?" "But don't we get acid rain here?" Donelle replied. "Maybe acid rain destroys stone."

The next day in school, Donelle described the "melting" statue to the class. Mr. Reynolds, their teacher, suggested that the class set up an experiment to find out what might be causing the damage to the statue. To begin, they came up with some questions that they wanted to answer.

What is destroying this statue?

Is rain destroying this statue?

Are cold winter temperatures destroying this statue?

The class decided that the first question was not specific enough. They decided to test whether rain could be destroying the statue. Students were curious about whether pollution in the air, and thus in the rain, might be affecting the statue.

Scientific investigations usually begin with something that you have noticed or read about. As you think about what you already know, you'll discover some ideas that you're not sure about. This will help you to ask the question that you really want to answer.

Before the class could begin setting up an experiment, there were some things they had to find out about the problem. First, they had to find out what the statue was made of. Ramon contacted City Hall and found out that the statue was made out of a stone called limestone.

Donelle told her classmates that she thought that the rain that fell on their town was sometimes acid. So Donelle and her classmates took samples of rainwater. They tested the rainwater with litmus paper and discovered that the rain was acidic.

The class thought about the new information they now had. It was time to use this information to formulate a hypothesis that they could test. Their hypothesis was "Acid rain eats away limestone."

When you use what you have observed to suggest a possible answer to your question, you are making a *hypothesis*. Be sure that your hypothesis is an idea that you can test somehow. If you can't think of an experiment or a model to test your hypothesis, try changing it. Sometimes it's better to make a simpler, clearer hypothesis that answers only part of your question.

H4

H5

Plan and Do a Test

Ramon, Donelle, and their classmates designed a way to test their hypothesis. First, Mr. Reynolds got some fairly equal-sized lumps of limestone for the class to use. Donelle set up three flat-bottomed beakers big enough to hold the chunks of limestone. Ramon created a table for recording information.

The students had discussed what kind of solutions they should use in each beaker. They decided to put rainwater they'd collected in one beaker. They decided to put a more acidic solution in the second beaker. Mr. Reynolds provided them with a solution of weak sulfuric acid. The students knew that the third beaker should contain only pure, distilled water.

The third beaker served as the students' control. The control part of an experiment is almost identical to the other parts of the experiment. It is different in just one way: it doesn't have the condition that is being tested. In this case, the class was testing the effects on limestone of water that is acidic. To make sure that their results only reflect the effects of acid, and not something else that might be in water, the students set up a control in which acid was missing.

After the three beakers were each filled with their specific liquid and labeled, the students found the mass of each chunk of limestone and then put one in each beaker.

The students placed the beakers on a lab table at the back of the classroom. A square piece of glass was placed over each beaker to keep out dirt and dust that might affect the results.

One way to try out your hypothesis is to use a test called an experiment. When you plan an experiment, be sure that it helps you to answer your question. But even when you plan, things can happen that make the experiment confusing or make it not work properly. If this happens, you can change the plan or the experiment, and try again.

Record and Analyze What Happened

After seven days, the mass of each limestone chunk was found again. The mass was recorded on the chart on the board. The chunk was replaced in the same beaker. This was repeated every seven days.

The students recorded the mass of the limestone chunks for fourteen weeks. At the end of the experiment, their chart looked like the one on the next page.

The students analyzed the data on their chart. Donelle noted that the more acidic the solution in the beaker, the more mass the limestone "lost." Ramon noted that the mass of the limestone in the beaker containing distilled water remained the same. The limestone in the rainwater beaker "lost" some mass, but not as much as the limestone chunk in the beaker containing sulfuric acid.

Mass of Limestone Each Week (in grams)

	Week													
	1	2	3	4	5	6	7	8	9	10	11	12	13	14
Rainwater	83	83	82	82	81	80	80	79	79	78	77	77	76	75
Sulfuric acid solution	76	74	71	69	68	65	63	60	59	55	53	50	48	45
Distilled water	79	79	79	79	79	79	79	79	79	79	79	79	79	79

When you do an experiment, you need to write down, or record, your observations. Some of your observations might be numbers of things that you counted or measured. Your recorded observations are called data. When you record your data, you need to organize it in a way that helps you to understand it. Graphs and tables are helpful ways to organize data. Then think about the information you have collected. Analyze what it tells you.

Draw Conclusions

Both Ramon and Donelle thought that it looked like their hypothesis was supported. Water containing an acid, or acid rain, did eat away limestone. But Ramon was still not completely satisfied. He wondered if acid rain affected all kinds of stone in the same way, or if it destroyed only limestone. Ramon posed his question to Mr. Reynolds and the other students. Then Patrick added, "And I wonder if cold weather makes the effects of acid rain even worse."

It was soon evident that though their experiment had showed that acid rain does affect limestone, a whole new set of questions occurred to them.

After you have analyzed your data, you should use what you have learned to draw a conclusion. A conclusion is a statement that sums up what you learned. The conclusion should be about the question you asked. Think about whether the information you have gathered supports your hypothesis or not. If it does, figure out how to test out your idea more thoroughly. Also think about new questions you can ask.

SAFETY

The best way to be safe in the classroom is to use common sense. Prepare yourself for each activity before you start it. Get help from your teacher when there is a problem. Most important of all, pay attention. Here are some other ways that you can stay safe.

Stay Safe From Stains

• Wear protective clothing or an old shirt when you work with messy materials.

• If anything spills, wipe it up or ask your teacher to help you clean it up.

Stay Safe From Flames

• Keep your clothes away from open flames. If you have long or baggy sleeves, roll them up.

• Don't let your hair get close to a flame. If you have long hair, tie it back.

Stay Safe During Cleanup

• Wash up after you finish working.

• Dispose of things in the way that your teacher tells you to.

Stay Safe From Injuries

• Protect your eyes by wearing safety goggles when you are told that you need them.

• Keep your hands dry around electricity. Water is a good conductor of electricity, so you can get a shock more easily if your hands are wet.

• Be careful with sharp objects. If you have to press on them, keep the sharp side away from you.

• Cover any cuts you have that are exposed. If you spill something on a cut, be sure to wash it off immediately.

• Don't eat or drink anything unless your teacher tells you that it's okay.

MOST IMPORTANTLY

If you ever hurt yourself or one of your group members gets hurt, tell your teacher right away.

DON'T MAKE A MESS If you spill something, clean it up right away. When finished with an activity, clean up your work area. Dispose of things in the way your teacher tells you to.

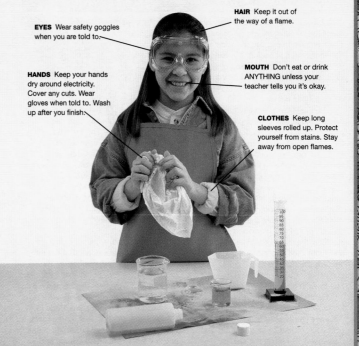

EYES Wear safety goggles when you are told to.

HAIR Keep it out of the way of a flame.

HANDS Keep your hands dry around electricity. Cover any cuts. Wear gloves when told to. Wash up after you finish.

MOUTH Don't eat or drink ANYTHING unless your teacher tells you it's okay.

CLOTHES Keep long sleeves rolled up. Protect yourself from stains. Stay away from open flames.

H8

H9

Using a
Microscope

A microscope makes it possible to see very small things by magnifying them. Some microscopes have a set of lenses to magnify objects different amounts.

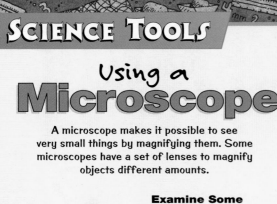

Examine Some Salt Grains

Handle a microscope carefully; it can break easily. Carry it firmly with both hands and avoid touching the lenses.

1. Turn the mirror toward a source of light. **NEVER** use the Sun as a light source.

2. Place a few grains of salt on the slide. Put the slide on the stage of the microscope.

3. While looking through the eyepiece, turn the adjustment knob on the back of the microscope to bring the salt grains into focus.

4. Raise the eyepiece tube to increase the magnification; lower it to decrease magnification.

H10

Using a
Calculator

After you've made measurements, a calculator can help you analyze your data. Some calculators have a memory key that allows you to save the result of one calculation while you do another.

Find an Average

The table shows the amount of rain that was collected using a rain gauge in each month of one year. You can use a calculator to help you find the average monthly rainfall.

1. Add the numbers. When you add a series of numbers, you don't need to press the equal sign until the last number is entered. Just press the plus sign after you enter each number (except the last one).

2. If you make a mistake while you are entering numbers, try to erase your mistake by pushing the clear entry (CE) key or the clear (C) key. Then you can continue entering the rest of the numbers you are adding. If you can't fix your mistake, you can push the (C) key once or twice until the screen shows 0. Then start over.

3. Your total should be 1,131. You can use the total to find the average. Just divide by the number of months in the year.

These keys run the calculator's memory functions.

This key erases the last entry.

Rainfall	
Month	Rain (mm)
Jan.	214
Feb.	138
Mar.	98
Apr.	157
May	84
June	41
July	5
Aug.	23
Sept.	48
Oct.	75
Nov.	140
Dec.	108

H11

Using a Balance

A balance is used to measure mass. Mass is the amount of matter in an object. Place the object to be massed in the left pan. Place standard masses in the right pan.

Measure the Mass of an Orange

1. Check that the empty pans are balanced, or level with each other. The pointer at the base should be on the middle mark. If it needs to be adjusted, move the slider on the back of the balance a little to the left or right.

2. Place an orange on the left pan. Notice that the pointer moves and that the pans are no longer level with each other. Then add standard masses, one at a time, to the right pan. When the pointer is at the middle mark again, the pans are balanced. Each pan holds the same amount of mass.

3. Each standard mass is marked to show the number of grams it contains. Add the number of grams marked on the masses in the pan. The total is the mass in grams of the orange.

Using a Spring Scale

A spring scale is used to measure force. You can use a spring scale to find the weight of an object in newtons. You can also use the scale to measure other forces.

Measure the Weight of an Object

1. Place the object in a net bag, and hang it from the hook on the bottom of the spring scale. Or, if possible, hang the object directly from the hook.

2. Slowly lift the scale by the top hook. Be sure the object to be weighed continues to hang from the bottom hook.

3. Wait until the pointer on the face of the spring scale has stopped moving. Read the number next to the pointer to determine the weight of the object in newtons.

Measure Friction

1. Hook the object to the bottom of the spring scale. Use a rubber band to connect the spring scale and object if needed.

2. Gently pull the top hook of the scale parallel to the floor. When the object starts to move, read the number of newtons next to the pointer on the scale. This number is the force of friction between the floor and the object as you drag the object.

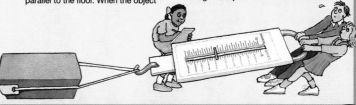

Using a Thermometer

A thermometer is used to measure temperature. When the liquid in the tube of a thermometer gets warmer, it expands and moves farther up the tube. Different units can be used to measure temperature, but scientists usually use the Celsius scale.

Measure the Temperature of a Cold Liquid

1. Half-fill a cup with chilled liquid.

2. Hold the thermometer so that the bulb is in the center of the liquid.

3. Wait until you see the liquid in the tube stop moving. Read the scale line that is closest to the top of the liquid in the tube.

Measuring Volume

A graduated cylinder, a measuring cup, and a beaker are used to measure volume. Volume is the amount of space something takes up. Most of the containers that scientists use to measure volume have a scale marked in milliliters (mL).

Measure the Volume of Juice

1. Pour the juice into a measuring container.

2. Move your head so that your eyes are level with the top of the juice. Read the scale line that is closest to the surface of the juice. If the surface of the juice is curved up on the sides, look at the lowest point of the curve.

3. You can estimate the value between two lines on the scale to obtain a more accurate measurement.

This graduated cylinder has marks for every 1 mL. ▶

This beaker has marks for each 25 mL. ▼

▲ The bottom of the curve is at 50 mL.

This measuring cup has marks for each 25 mL. ▼

Each container above has 50 mL of juice.

H14

H15

MEASUR EMENTS

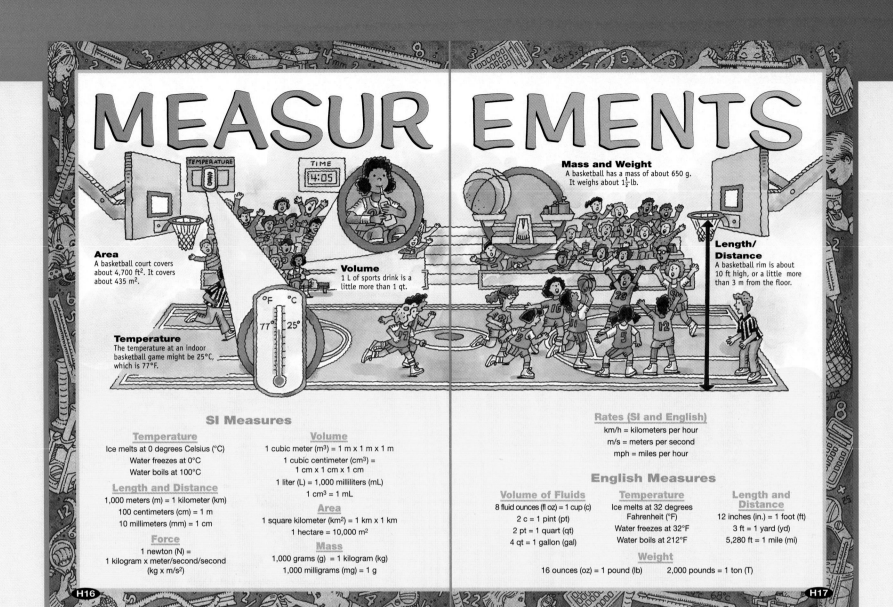

Area
A basketball court covers about 4,700 ft². It covers about 435 m².

Temperature
The temperature at an indoor basketball game might be 25°C, which is 77°F.

Volume
1 L of sports drink is a little more than 1 qt.

Mass and Weight
A basketball has a mass of about 650 g. It weighs about 1½ lb.

Length/ Distance
A basketball rim is about 10 ft high, or a little more than 3 m from the floor.

SI Measures

Temperature
Ice melts at 0 degrees Celsius (°C)

Water freezes at 0°C

Water boils at 100°C

Length and Distance
1,000 meters (m) = 1 kilometer (km)

100 centimeters (cm) = 1 m

10 millimeters (mm) = 1 cm

Force
1 newton (N) =
1 kilogram x meter/second/second
(kg x m/s²)

Volume
1 cubic meter (m³) = 1 m x 1 m x 1 m

1 cubic centimeter (cm³) =
1 cm x 1 cm x 1 cm

1 liter (L) = 1,000 milliliters (mL)

1 cm³ = 1 mL

Area
1 square kilometer (km²) = 1 km x 1 km

1 hectare = 10,000 m²

Mass
1,000 grams (g) = 1 kilogram (kg)

1,000 milligrams (mg) = 1 g

Rates (SI and English)
km/h = kilometers per hour

m/s = meters per second

mph = miles per hour

English Measures

Volume of Fluids
8 fluid ounces (fl oz) = 1 cup (c)

2 c = 1 pint (pt)

2 pt = 1 quart (qt)

4 qt = 1 gallon (gal)

Temperature
Ice melts at 32 degrees
Fahrenheit (°F)

Water freezes at 32°F

Water boils at 212°F

Length and Distance
12 inches (in.) = 1 foot (ft)

3 ft = 1 yard (yd)

5,280 ft = 1 mile (mi)

Weight
16 ounces (oz) = 1 pound (lb)   2,000 pounds = 1 ton (T)

GLOSSARY

Pronunciation Key

Symbol	Key Words	Symbol	Key Words
a	cat	g	get
ā	ape	h	help
ä	cot, car	j	jump
		k	kiss, call
e	ten, berry	l	leg
ē	me	m	meat
		n	nose
i	fit, here	p	put
ī	ice, fire	r	red
		s	see
ō	go	t	top
ô	fall, for	v	vat
oi	oil	w	wish
ᴏᴏ	look, pull	y	yard
ᴏ̄ᴏ̄	tool, rule	z	zebra
ou	out, crowd		
		ch	chin, arch
u	up	ŋ	ring, drink
ʉ	fur, shirt	sh	she, push
		th	thin, truth
ə	a in ago	*th*	then, father
	e in agent	zh	measure
	i in pencil		
	o in atom	A heavy stress mark ′ is placed after a syllable that gets a heavy, or primary, stress, as in **picture** (pik′chər).
	u in circus	
b	bed	
d	dog	
f	fall	

—— A ——

absolute age The actual age of an object. (E79) The *absolute age* of this statue is 3,500 years.

absolute magnitude The measure of a star's brightness, based on the amount of light it actually gives off. (B61) The Sun's *absolute magnitude* is less than that of many stars, but its apparent magnitude exceeds that of any other star.

adaptation (ad əp tā′shən) A structure or behavior that enables an organism to survive in its environment. (A70, A86) The thick fur of some animals is an *adaptation* to cold environments.

addiction (ə dik′shən) A condition in which a person has extreme difficulty in stopping the use of a drug. (G51) Sometimes it takes only a short time to develop an *addiction* to a drug.

alcohol (al′kə hôl) A drug that is found in some beverages, such as beer and wine. (G50) If a person drinks *alcohol* to excess, problems can occur.

alcoholism (al′kə hôl iz əm) A disease that results from the continual misuse of alcohol. (G60) Doctors continue to learn more about *alcoholism*.

amplitude (am′plə tᴏ̄ᴏ̄d) A measure of the amount of energy in a sound wave. (F57) The *amplitude* of a loud sound is greater than the amplitude of a soft sound.

anticline (an′ti klīn) An upward fold of rock layers. (E84) Bending layers of rock formed an *anticline*.

eroded anticline

apparent magnitude The measure of a star's brightness as seen from Earth. (B61) A star's *apparent magnitude* depends on the amount of light it gives off and on its distance from Earth.

asexual reproduction (ā sek′shᴏ̄ᴏ̄ əl rē prə duk′shən) A process in which offspring are produced from one or more cells of a single parent. (A62) In *asexual reproduction*, the offspring is identical to the parent.

audiocassette (ô′dē ō kə set) A small container holding magnetic tape that is used for playing or recording sound. (F92) We inserted an *audiocassette* into the tape recorder.

auditory nerve (ô′də tôr ē nʉrv) A nerve in the ear that carries nerve impulses to the brain. (G39, F85) The *auditory nerve* contains sensory neurons.

axis The imaginary line on which an object rotates. (B13) Earth's *axis* runs between the North and South poles.

H19

Big Bang Theory A hypothesis, supported by data, that describes how the universe began with a huge explosion. (B39) The *Big Bang Theory* holds that everything in the universe was once concentrated at one tiny point.

biodiversity (bī ō də vʉr'sə tē) The variety of organisms that live in Earth's many ecosystems; the variety of plants and animals that live within a particular ecosystem. (D58) The *biodiversity* of an ecosystem quickly changes after a natural disaster.

biome (bī'ōm) A major land ecosystem having a distinct combination of plants and animals. (D48) Some *biomes*, such as the tundra, do not easily support human populations.

biosphere (bī'ō sfir) A self-sustaining natural system of living things and their environment. (B87) For humans to survive in space, they must bring along a version of their *biosphere*.

black dwarf The cool, dark body that is the final stage in the life cycle of a low-mass star. (B66) When the Sun dies, it will become a *black dwarf*.

black hole An extremely dense, invisible object in space whose gravity is so great that not even light can escape it. (B67) Scientists think that the remains of a very massive star can collapse following a supernova explosion to form a *black hole*.

blood alcohol concentration A test that determines the level of alcohol in a person's blood. (G61) A police officer can easily find out if a driver is drunk by giving a *blood alcohol concentration* test.

bone The hard tissue that forms the skeleton. Also, one of the organs that makes up the skeleton. (G8) The human hand contains many small *bones*.

caffeine (ka fēn') A drug that acts as a stimulant and is present in coffee, many teas, cocoa, and some soft drinks. (G50) Many people prefer to drink herbal teas that do not have *caffeine* in them.

carbon dioxide–oxygen cycle See oxygen–carbon dioxide cycle.

cardiac muscle (kär'dē ak mus'əl) Involuntary muscle tissue that makes up the heart. (G17) *Cardiac muscle* contracts rhythmically.

carnivore (kär'nə vôr) A consumer that eats only other animals. (D19, D30) Lions are *carnivores* that prey on zebras and other large plant eaters.

cartilage (kärt'əl ij) Tough, flexible tissue that is part of the skeleton. (G8) *Cartilage* helps protect bones as they move at joints.

cell The basic unit of structure of all living things. (A24) Even though plant *cells* can be different sizes, they still have many of the same structures.

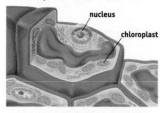

nucleus
chloroplast

cell membrane A thin layer that surrounds all cells and allows water and dissolved materials to pass into and out of the cell. (A24) In plant cells, the *cell membrane* lies inside the cell wall.

cell respiration The process of using oxygen to release energy from food. (A35, A45, D34) Animals and plants release carbon dioxide as a waste product of *cell respiration*.

cell wall The tough outer covering of a plant cell that gives the cell its rigid shape. (A24) A *cell wall* is not found in animal cells.

cementation (sē men tā'shən) A process in which minerals, deposited as water evaporates, bind sediments into solid rock. (E44) Sandstone is a sedimentary rock formed by *cementation*.

cerebellum (ser ə bel'əm) The second largest part of the brain, coordinating the body's muscles. (G32) The *cerebellum* allows smooth movement.

cerebrum (sə rē'brəm) The largest part of the brain in which the processes of thinking, learning, and reasoning take place. (G31) The *cerebrum* is the part of the brain that allows people to understand and remember ideas.

chloroplast (klôr'ə plast) A structure in plant cells that captures light energy that is used in the food-making process. (A24, A33) *Chloroplasts* are located within cells in the leaves of a plant.

cleavage (klēv'ij) The tendency of some minerals to split along flat surfaces. (E15) Salt, or halite, shows *cleavage* in three planes.

clone (klōn) An exact copy of a parent organism produced by asexual reproduction. (A62) One way to *clone* a parent plant is to place a cutting from that plant in water.

coastal ocean A saltwater ecosystem that is relatively shallow and close to the shoreline and that supports an abundance of life. (D54) The *coastal ocean* is an ecosystem that lies beyond the shoreline.

comet (käm'it) A small object in space, made of ice, dust, gas, and rock, that orbits a star and that can form a gaseous tail. (B24) As a *comet* approaches the Sun, it begins to melt.

commensalism (kə men′səl iz əm) A close relationship between two kinds of organisms that benefits one of the organisms while neither benefiting nor hurting the other. (D21) The way that some insects use their resemblance to plants to hide from predators is an example of *commensalism*.

community (kə myoo′nə tē) All the organisms living together in a particular ecosystem. (D10) Raccoons, deer, and trees are part of a forest *community*.

compact disc (käm′pakt disk) A small disk on which sounds are digitally recorded and played back when read by a laser beam. (F92) This *compact disc*, or CD, contains one hour of music.

compound machine A machine that is made up of two or more simple machines. (C62) A pair of scissors is a *compound machine* because it contains two kinds of simple machines—a lever and a wedge.

compound microscope A viewing instrument that uses two lenses to magnify objects many times. (F41) The human hair appeared 1,000 times larger than actual size under the *compound microscope*.

compression (kəm presh′ən) A region in a sound wave where particles have been pushed together. (F57) The *compressions* produced by a vibrating tuning fork are areas of greater than normal air pressure.

concave lens (kän′kāv lenz) A lens that is thicker at the edges than it is in the middle and that causes light rays to spread apart. (F32) A *concave lens* is used to correct nearsightedness.

concave mirror A mirror that curves inward at the middle. (F23) A *concave mirror* is used in a reflecting telescope.

concrete (kän′krēt) A mixture of rock material and cement that is used as a building material. (E24) This sidewalk is made of *concrete*.

condensation (kän dən sā′shən) The process by which water vapor is changed to liquid water. (D36) *Condensation* can occur on a glass containing ice cubes.

conduction (kən duk′shən) The transfer of heat energy by direct contact between particles. (C13) Heat travels through a metal by *conduction*.

conifer (kän′ə fər) A tree or shrub that bears its seeds in cones. (A80) The cones of each species of *conifer* are distinct and different from each other.

constellation (kän stə lā′shən) A group of stars that form a fixed pattern in the night sky. (B10) The *constellation* Orion is best seen in the winter.

consumer (kən soom′ər) A living thing that obtains energy by eating other living things. (A36, D19) Meat eaters and plant eaters are *consumers*.

contact lens A thin lens worn over the cornea of the eye, usually to correct vision problems. (F35) Some people use *contact lenses* rather than eyeglasses to improve their vision.

convection (kən vek′shən) The transfer of heat energy through liquids and gases by moving particles. (C13) Heat is carried throughout water in a pot on the stove by *convection*.

convex lens (kän′veks lenz) A lens that is thicker in the middle than at the edges and that brings light rays together. (F32) A *convex lens* is used to correct farsightedness.

convex mirror A mirror that curves outward at the middle. (F23) The side-view mirror of a car is a *convex mirror*.

core The innermost layer of Earth, which consists of a molten outer part and a solid inner part. (E69) Temperatures inside the *core* of Earth are nearly as hot as those on the Sun's surface.

crest The highest point of a wave. (F57) The top of a water wave is its *crest*.

crust The outer layer of Earth. (E68) Earth's *crust* is a thin layer of rock.

cytoplasm (sīt′ō plaz əm) The jellylike substance that fills much of the cell. (A24) The nucleus, vacuoles, and many other cell structures float in the *cytoplasm*.

decibel (des′ə bəl) A unit used to measure the loudness or intensity of sound. (F79) Sounds that have an intensity greater than 120 *decibels* (db) can hurt your ears.

decomposer (dē kəm pōz′ər) A living thing that breaks down the remains of dead organisms. (A37, D19) *Decomposers*, such as bacteria, get their energy from the dead plants and animals they break down.

deciduous forest (dē sij′oo əs fôr′ist) A biome that contains many trees and in which rainfall is moderate. (D51) *Deciduous forests* support a great variety of animal life.

deforestation (dē fôr is tā′shən) A mass clearing of a forest. (A93) *Deforestation* is a major concern of environmentalists.

desert A biome in which plant life is not abundant and rainfall is low. (D50) Because *deserts* are dry, desert plants have adaptations to conserve water.

dicot (dī′kät) A flowering plant that produces seeds with two seed leaves, or food-storing leaves. (A81) A trait of a *dicot* is that its leaves have netlike veins.

drug A substance, other than food, that can affect the function of body cells and tissues and that produces a change in the body. (G50) A person sometimes takes a pain-killing *drug* after suffering a back injury.

ecosystem (ek'ō sis təm) An area in which living and nonliving things interact. (D10) An oak tree and the organisms that inhabit it can be thought of as a small *ecosystem*.

effort force The force that must be applied to an object to move the object. (C30) The tow truck applied enough *effort force* to pull the car away.

electromagnetic radiation (ē lek trō-mag net'ik rā dē ā'shən) Wave energy given off by the Sun and some other objects. (F8) Visible light is a form of *electromagnetic radiation*.

electron microscope (ē lek'trän mī'krə skōp) A viewing instrument that magnifies objects thousands of times by using a beam of electrons instead of a beam of light. (F43) Doctors studied the virus through an *electron microscope*.

embryo (em'brē ō) An organism in its earliest stages of development; in most plants it is found inside a seed. (A61) When conditions for growth are suitable, the *embryo* inside the seed develops into a young plant.

endangered In danger of becoming extinct. (A92, D61) As the destruction of the Amazon rain forest continues, the number of *endangered* species increases.

energy The ability to do work or cause change. (C9, F8) *Energy* from the Sun warms the air.

erosion (ē rō'zhən) The wearing away and removing of rock and soil caused by such forces as wind and flowing water. (E84) The pounding waves caused *erosion* of the sandy shoreline.

eustachian tube (yōō stā'kē ən tōōb) A tube that connects the throat and the middle ear. (F85) The *eustachian tube* equalizes the air pressure on both sides of the eardrum.

evaporation (ē vap ə rā'shən) The process by which liquid water changes to water vapor. (D36) One phase of the water cycle is the *evaporation* of water from lakes, rivers, and oceans.

extinct (ek stiŋkt') No longer living as a species. (A92, D61) Traces of some *extinct* species can be found in fossils.

extraterrestrial (eks trə tə res'trē əl) A being from outer space; any object from beyond Earth. (B90) It would be extraordinary for scientists to discover that there is *extraterrestrial* life.

fault A break in rock along which rocks have moved. (E91) Forces within Earth's crust produce *faults*.

fern A nonseed plant that has roots, stems, and leaves and that is found mostly in moist, shady areas. (A79) On *ferns* that grow in tropical places, the fronds grow to a very tall size.

fertilization (furt 'l ə zā'shən) The process by which a male sex cell joins with a female sex cell. In flowering plants, fertilization takes place in the pistil. (A60) *Fertilization* occurs after a pollen tube reaches the ovary.

filter A device that lets certain colors of light pass through while absorbing others. (F48) The stage manager placed a red *filter* over the spotlight.

flower The reproductive structure of a flowering plant. (A16) Petals protect the reproductive parts of a *flower*.

flowering plant Living organisms that reproduce by seeds formed in flowers and that have roots, stems, and leaves. (A81) *Flowering plants* are the most common group of plants on Earth today.

focal point The point at which light rays passing through a lens come together. (F32) Rays of light meet at the *focal point*.

fold A bend in a layer of rock. (E83) Forces within Earth can cause a *fold* to form in rock layers.

food chain The path of energy transfer from one living organism to another in an ecosystem. (A36, D29) Energy moves from producers to consumers in a *food chain*.

food web The overlapping food chains that link producers, consumers, and decomposers in an ecosystem. (A37, D30) Some consumers in a *food web* eat both plants and animals.

force A pull or a push. (C28) When you open a door, you apply a *force*.

fossil (fäs'əl) The remains or traces of a living thing from the past, preserved in rock. (E46, E77) *Fossils* can include imprints of animal skeletons pressed into rock.

fracture (frak'chər) A break or crack in a bone. (G20) The skier suffered a leg *fracture* when he hit an icy patch.

free fall The motion of a freely falling object, such as a spacecraft in orbit around Earth. (B79) Astronauts experiencing *free fall* in space feel weightless.

frequency (frē'kwən sē) The number of waves (such as light or sound) produced in a unit of time, such as a second. (F18, F57) The *frequency* of light waves varies with the color of the light.

friction (frik'shən) Force produced by the rubbing of one thing against another; a force that acts to oppose motion. (C31) *Friction* prevents sneakers from slipping on a gym floor.

fruit The enlarged ovary of a flower that protects the developing seeds. (A61) Some *fruits*, such as peaches or mangoes, contain only one seed.

fulcrum (ful'krəm) The fixed point around which a lever pivots. (C50) If you use a lever to lift an object, the *fulcrum* is located between you and the object you are lifting.

galaxy (gal'ək sē) A vast group of billions of stars that are held together by gravity. (B70) The Milky Way is a typical spiral *galaxy*.

gas giant A large planet that is made up mostly of gaseous and liquid substances, with little or no solid surface. (B47) Jupiter is a *gas giant*.

geocentric model (jē ō sen'trik mäd''l) A representation of the universe in which stars and planets revolve around Earth. (B37) Ptolemy proposed a *geocentric model* of the universe.

glucose (glo͞o'kōs) A sugar produced by plants that is the main source of energy for cells. (A33) *Glucose* is produced during photosynthesis.

grassland A biome containing many grasses but few trees and having low to moderate rainfall. (D50) Taller grasses occur in *grasslands* that have more abundant rainfall.

hardness A measure of how easily a mineral can be scratched. (E13) The *hardness* of diamond is greater than that of any other mineral.

hearing aid A small battery-powered electronic device that makes sounds louder. (F86) Most people who wear a *hearing aid* have improved hearing.

heliocentric model (hē lē ō sen'trik mäd''l) A representation of the relationship between the Sun and planets in which the planets revolve around the Sun. (B37) Copernicus hypothesized a *heliocentric model* of the solar system.

herbivore (hʉr'bə vôr) A consumer that eats only plants or other producers. (D19, D30) Panda bears are *herbivores* that have a very limited diet because they only eat bamboo.

hertz (herts) A unit used to measure wave frequency. (F18, F68) If 100 waves are produced per second, the frequency of the wave is 100 *hertz*.

igneous rock (ig'nē əs räk) A type of rock that forms from melted rock that cools and hardens. (E40) *Igneous rock* forms from both magma and lava.

illegal drug A substance whose use is prohibited by law. (G50) One *illegal drug* in the United States is heroin.

inclined plane A simple machine with a sloping surface. It allows objects to be raised or lowered from one level to another without lifting them. (C43) A ramp is a kind of *inclined plane*.

index fossil (in'deks fäs'əl) A fossil used to determine the relative age of rock. (E78) The remains of a living thing that lived only at a certain time in the past makes a good *index fossil*.

information superhighway The futuristic concept of communications as an electronic highway system in which telephones, computers, and televisions are linked. (F93) The *information superhighway* will let students do library research from their homes.

intensity (in ten'sə tē) A measure of the amount of energy of sound. (F78) A sound that has high *intensity* is loud enough to be heard from a distance.

Internet (in'tər net) A system of interconnected computer networks. (F94) Telephone lines link computer users with the *Internet*.

joint The place where two bones meet. (G8) Your elbow *joint* enables you to bend your arm.

joule (jo͞ol) The basic unit of energy and of work. (C19) Scientists measure amounts of energy in *joules*.

kinetic energy The energy that something has because of its motion. (C20) As a boulder rolls down a steep hill, it gains *kinetic energy*.

lake A freshwater ecosystem characterized by still, or standing water. (D53) *Lakes* support fish, birds, algae, and other forms of life.

lava (lä'və) Melted rock material that reaches Earth's surface before it cools and hardens. (E41) A volcano carries *lava* to Earth's surface.

leaf A plant part in which photosynthesis takes place. (A14) In a plant such as cabbage, it is the *leaf* that people eat.

lens A piece of glass or other transparent material with at least one curved surface that brings together or spreads apart light rays passing through it. (F32) The *lens* in a camera focuses an image on the film.

lever (lev′ər) A simple machine made up of a bar that pivots around a fixed point (a fulcrum). (C50) A *lever* can help lift a heavy object with less effort.

ligament (lig′ə mənt) A band of strong tissue that connects bones and holds them in place. (G8) A *ligament* holds bones together at a joint.

light-year A unit of measurement representing the distance that light travels in one year. (B61) Scientists use the unit called a *light-year* when measuring the distances to stars.

luster (lus′tər) The way that the surface of a mineral looks when it reflects light. (E13) Silver and gold have a shiny, metallic *luster*.

machine A device that makes work easier by reducing the amount of force needed to do a job. (C43) A *machine* can make it easier to move, lift, carry, or cut something.

magma (mag′mə) Melted rock material that forms deep within Earth. (E40) Some igneous rocks, such as granite, form from *magma*.

mantle A thick layer of rock between the crust and the core of Earth. (E69) The top of the *mantle* is solid rock but below that is a section of rock that can flow.

mechanical advantage (mə kan′i-kəl ad vant′ij) The number of times that a machine multiplies the effort force applied to it. (C44) To find the *mechanical advantage* of an inclined plane, divide the length of its sloping surface by its height.

medulla (mi dul′ə) The part of the brain that controls the involuntary functions of the body, such as heart rate and breathing. (G32) The *medulla* is located in the brain stem and controls many things you do without thinking.

metamorphic rock (met ə môr′fik räk) A type of rock that forms from existing rocks because of changes caused by heat, pressure, or chemicals. (E47) Slate is a *metamorphic rock* that forms from the sedimentary rock shale.

meteor (mēt′ē ər) A piece of rock or metal from space that enters Earth's atmosphere. (B25) A *meteor* appears as a streak of light, which is why it is also called a shooting star.

meteorite (mēt′ē ər īt) The remaining material of a meteor that has landed on the ground. (B25) In 1902, scientists were able to examine the largest *meteorite* ever known to land in the United States.

Milky Way Galaxy A gigantic cluster of billions of stars that is home to our solar system. (B70) The Sun is located in one of the arms of the *Milky Way Galaxy*.

mineral A solid element or compound found in nature and having a definite chemical composition and crystal structure. (E12) Quartz is a *mineral*.

model Something used or made to represent an object or an idea. (E68) The plastic *model* was a miniature copy of the actual airplane.

monocot (män′ō kät) A flowering plant that produces seeds with a single seed leaf, or food-storing leaf. (A81) About one third of all flowering plants are *monocots*.

moon A natural object that revolves around a planet. (B44) The planet Mars has two known *moons*.

moss A small nonseed plant that lacks roots, stems, and leaves and grows mostly in moist areas in woods or near stream banks. (A78) The leaflike part of a *moss* only grows a few centimeters above ground.

motor neuron (mōt′ər nōō′rän) A nerve cell that carries impulses from the brain and spinal cord to muscles and glands in the body. (G28) When people exercise, *motor neurons* carry impulses from the spinal cord to different muscles in the body.

mutualism (myōō′chōō əl iz əm) A close relationship between two or more organisms in which all organisms benefit. (D22) Bees carrying pollen from flower to flower as they obtain nectar is an example of *mutualism*.

narcotic (när kät′ik) A habit-forming drug that depresses the function of the nervous system. (G55) Morphine is a *narcotic* drug that is often given to cancer patients.

nebula (neb′yə lə) A huge cloud of gas and dust found in space. (B64) A *nebula* can form when a supernova explodes.

nerve impulse (nʉrv im′puls) A message carried through the body by neurons. (G28) *Nerve impulses* pass from one neuron to another as they move through the body.

neuron (nōō′rän) A nerve cell. (G28) The brain is connected to all parts of the body by *neurons*.

neutron star (nōō′trän stär) The remains of a massive star that has exploded in a supernova. (B67) A typical *neutron star* is less than 20 km in diameter.

newton A unit used to measure force. (C29) About 300 *newtons* of force was applied in moving the rock.

nicotine (nik′ə tēn) A drug found in the tobacco plant. (G50) People become addicted to cigarettes because of the *nicotine* in the tobacco.

nitrogen cycle The cycle through which nitrogen gas is changed into compounds that can be used by living things and then is returned to the atmosphere. (D42) The *nitrogen cycle* is of great importance to all life forms because nitrogen is needed to make protein.

noise pollution The occurrence of loud or unpleasant sound in the environment. (F80) The sounds of city traffic are a form of *noise pollution*.

nonseed plant A plant that reproduces without forming seeds. (A78) Mosses are *nonseed plants*.

nucleus (nōō′klē əs) The cell structure that controls all of a cell's activities. (A24) The *nucleus* was clearly visible after it was stained.

octave (äk′tiv) The series of eight notes that makes up a musical scale. (F69) The music student practiced playing *octaves* on the piano.

omnivore (äm′ni vôr) A consumer that eats both plants and animals. (D19, D30) Because they eat both meats and vegetables, many humans are *omnivores*.

opaque (ō pāk′) Not letting light through. (F47) The *opaque* curtains kept out the sunlight.

open ocean A large saltwater ecosystem containing both floating and free-swimming organisms. (D55) The *open ocean* covers much of Earth's surface.

optic nerve A bundle of neurons that carries impulses from the eye to the brain. (G39) If there is damage to the *optic nerve,* messages from the eye cannot be received by the brain.

ore (ôr) A mineral or rock that contains enough of a metal to making mining the metal profitable. (E27) Hematite is an *ore* mined for its iron content.

overtone A fainter, higher tone that harmonizes with the main tone produced by a musical instrument or the human voice. (F58) The blending of *overtones* gives the flute its unique sound.

oxygen–carbon dioxide cycle A natural cycle in which plants and other producers use carbon dioxide and produce oxygen, and living things use oxygen and produce carbon dioxide. (B86, D34) The *oxygen–carbon dioxide cycle* must be duplicated in space if humans wish to make long voyages to other planets.

parasitism (par′ə sīt iz əm) A relationship between two organisms in which one organism lives on or in the other, feeds upon it, and usually harms it. (D21) The way in which fleas live off dogs is an example of *parasitism*.

phloem cell (flō′əm sel) A plant cell that, when linked with other similar cells, forms a system of tubes for carrying nutrients from the leaves down through the stem and root. (A11) The *phloem cells* form a major transport system in plants.

phonograph (fō′nə graf) A device that reproduces sounds recorded on a disk. (F90) We played old records on the *phonograph*.

photosynthesis (fōt ō sin′thə sis) The process by which producers, such as plants, make their own food by using energy from the Sun. (A33) *Photosynthesis* takes place primarily in the leaves of plants.

pistil (pis′til) The female reproductive structure of a flower. (A16) A *pistil* consists of three main parts—the stigma, the style, and the ovary.

pitch The highness or lowness of a sound. (F68) A tuba produces sounds with a low *pitch*.

plane mirror A mirror that has a flat surface. (F22) The mirror over the bathroom sink is a *plane mirror*.

planet A large body in space that orbits a star and does not produce light on its own. (B17) Earth is one of nine known *planets* that revolve around the Sun.

plant kingdom A major group of living things that are multicellular and that carry out photosynthesis. (A78) Living organisms in the *plant kingdom* make their own food.

pollination (päl ə nā′shən) The transfer of pollen from the male part of one flower to the female part of another flower. (A60) Some *pollination* is done by insects.

population (päp yōō lā′shən) A group of the same kind of organisms that live in an area. (D10) There is a huge *population* of frogs in that marsh.

potential energy The energy that an object has because of its position or structure; stored energy. (C18) A coiled spring has *potential energy*.

precipitation (prē sip ə tā′shən) The process by which water from clouds falls back to the Earth. (D36) *Precipitation* falls to the Earth in the form of rain or snow.

producer (prō dōōs′ər) An organism that makes its own food through photosynthesis. (A36, D18) Plants and algae are examples of *producers*.

protein (prō′tēn) Organic compounds that form the structure and control the processes that take place in living things. (D41) *Proteins* provide the body with materials that help cells grow and repair themselves.

protostar (prōt′ō stär) A concentration of matter found in space that is the beginning of a star. (B64) When the temperature inside a *protostar* becomes high enough, nuclear reactions begin and it turns into a star.

pulley (pōōl′ē) A simple machine made up of a wheel around which a rope or chain is passed. (C53) A *pulley* helps lift objects that would be too heavy to lift directly.

quarry (kwôr′ē) A mine, usually near or at Earth's surface, from which rock is removed. (E52) Granite, sandstone, limestone, slate, and marble are some rocks that come from a *quarry*.

radiation (rā dē ā′shən) The transfer of energy by waves. (C11) Energy given off by the Sun travels as *radiation* through space.

radio telescope A gigantic antenna designed to receive radio signals from space. (B92) *Radio telescopes* are important tools for studying distant stars and galaxies.

rarefaction (rer ə fak′shən) A region in a sound wave where there are fewer particles than normal. (F57) The *rarefactions* that a vibrating violin string produces are areas of lower than normal air pressure.

receptor (ri sep′tər) A sensory neuron that receives stimuli from the environment. (G37) Sensory *receptors* in the skin make it possible for people to feel heat, cold, pressure, touch, and pain.

red giant A very large old reddish star that has greatly expanded and cooled as its fuel has begun to run out. (B65) As the Sun reaches old age, it will turn into a *red giant*.

reflecting telescope An instrument for viewing distant objects that uses a curved mirror at the back of its tube to gather light and produce an image. (B22, F39) This observatory uses a *reflecting telescope* to observe faraway galaxies.

reflection (ri flek′shən) The bouncing of light or sound off a surface. (F22) The *reflection* of sunlight off the snow made us squint.

reflex (rē′fleks) A simple behavior pattern involving an automatic response to a stimulus. (G42) The girl's automatic *reflex* quickly got her foot out of the hot water.

refracting telescope An instrument for viewing distant objects that uses two lenses to gather light and produce an image. (B21) The *refracting telescope* gave us a closer look at the Moon.

refraction (ri frak′shən) The bending of light as it passes from one material into another. (F24) Light traveling from air into water will undergo *refraction*.

relative age The age of an object as compared to other objects. (E78) The order of layers of rock shows the *relative ages* of the layers.

resistance force A force that resists, or opposes, motion. (C30) Friction is a *resistance force*.

retina (ret′′n ə) The light-sensitive area at the back of the eye on which an image is formed. (F32) The *retina* contains two kinds of cells.

revolution (rev ə lōō′shən) The movement of an object around another object or point. (B14) It takes about 365 days for Earth to make one *revolution* around the Sun.

river A freshwater ecosystem characterized by running water. (D52) Salmon are able to swim against the current in a *river*.

rock The solid material composed of minerals that forms Earth's crust. Also, the material, sometimes molten, that forms Earth's inner layers. (E40) *Rocks* are weathered by wind and rain.

rock cycle The continuous series of changes that rocks undergo. (E60) In the *rock cycle*, changes are brought about by factors such as weathering, melting, cooling, or pressure.

root The underground part of a plant that anchors the plant and absorbs water and nutrients. (A10) Carrots and turnips have only one large single *root*.

rotation (rō tā′shən) The spinning motion of an object on its axis. (B14) It takes about 24 hours for Earth to make one complete *rotation*.

sapling (sap′liŋ) A young tree. (A67) The year after a tree seed germinates, the young plant is called a *sapling*.

satellite (sat′′l īt) A natural or human-built object that revolves around another object in space. (B44) The Moon is a natural *satellite* of Earth.

sediment (sed′ə mənt) Bits of weathered rocks and minerals and pieces of dead plants or animals. (E43) Over time, *sediments* can form sedimentary rocks, such as sandstone and limestone.

sedimentary rock (sed ə men′tər ē räk) A type of rock that forms when sediments harden. (E43) Most *sedimentary rocks* form in layers.

seed coat A tough, protective covering on a seed, enclosing the embryo and its food supply. (A 61) When the leaves on a young plant start to grow and open up, the *seed coat* falls off.

seed dispersal The scattering of seeds away from the parent plant. (A88) The wind is one way in which *seed dispersal* is carried out.

seed leaf A first leaf found inside a seed, providing food for the tiny developing plant. (A66) A monocot seed contains one *seed leaf*.

seedling (sēd′liŋ) A young growing plant after it first sprouts and develops new leaves. (A66) In spring the forest floor is covered with green *seedlings*.

seed plant A plant that reproduces by forming seeds. (A78) Corn and wheat are *seed plants*.

semicircular canal Any of three curved tubelike structures of the inner ear that help the body to maintain balance. (F85) The *semicircular canals* respond to movements of the head.

sensory neuron (sen′sər ē noo′rän) A nerve cell that carries impulses from the senses to the brain and spinal cord. (G28) *Sensory neurons* carry impulses from your eyes to your brain.

sexual reproduction The production of offspring that occurs when a male sex cell joins a female sex cell. (A59) The *sexual reproduction* of flowers is greatly aided by insects.

shoreline The ecosystem where land and ocean meet. (D54) The *shoreline* varies in width around the world.

simple microscope A microscope that uses a single lens to magnify objects. (F41) A magnifying glass is a *simple microscope.*

skeletal muscle Voluntary muscle tissue; also, one of the muscles that moves bones. (G17) Tendons attach *skeletal muscles* to bones.

skeletal system The system of bones and tissues that supports and protects the body. (G8) The human *skeletal system* contains 206 bones.

smelting (smelt′iŋ) The process of melting ore to remove the metal from it. (E28) Workers obtain iron by *smelting* iron ore in a blast furnace.

smooth muscle Involuntary muscle tissue that lines the inside of blood vessels, intestines, and other organs. (G17) *Smooth muscles* move food through the digestive system.

solar system The Sun and the planets and other objects that orbit the Sun. Also, any star and the objects that revolve around it. (B34) Our *solar system* consists of the Sun, nine known planets, and many smaller objects.

sound A form of energy that travels through matter as waves. (F56) The *sound* made the floor vibrate.

sound synthesizer (sound sin′thə-sī zər) An electronic device that can produce a wide variety of sounds. (F71) The composer used a *sound synthesizer* to create a new musical composition.

sprain An injury in which the ligament at a joint is torn or twisted. (G19) An ankle *sprain* can take weeks to heal.

stamen (stā′mən) The male reproductive structure of a flower. (A16) Pollen is produced in the *stamens.*

star A huge object in space, made up of hot gases, that shines by its own light. (B17) Many *stars* are believed to have systems of planets.

starch (stärch) A substance found in plants that is a storage form of glucose. (A35) Potatoes contain a lot of *starch.*

stem The part of a plant that supports the leaves and flowers and carries water to these parts of the plant. (A12) The trunk of a tree is a *stem.*

steroid (stir′oid) A drug that helps to build up muscle tissue and strength. (G55) Some athletes have used *steroids.*

stimulant (stim′yoo lənt) A drug that increases the activity of the nervous system. (G55) Many people drink coffee because it acts as a *stimulant.*

stimulus (stim′yoo ləs) An event or environmental condition that triggers a nerve impulse, thus causing an organism to respond. (G28) The *stimulus* of a loud sound can make a person jump.

stoma (stō′mə; *pl.* stō ma′tə) One of many small openings, or pores, usually on the underside of a leaf, through which gases enter and leave a plant. (A46) The *stomata* on a water lily are on the top of the leaf.

strain An injury in which a muscle or tendon is torn slightly or stretched too far. (G20) Lifting the heavy couch gave me a back *strain.*

streak (strēk) The colored powder made by rubbing a mineral against a ceramic surface. (E15) Although pyrite is yellow, it produces a black *streak.*

substance abuse (sub′stəns ə-byoos′) The improper use, or abuse, of alcohol or drugs. (G50) *Substance abuse* can damage a person's health.

supernova (soo′pər nō və) An exploding star. (B66) When a red giant star uses up all its fuel, it collapses and explodes in a *supernova.*

syncline (sin′klīn) A downward fold of rock layers. (E84) Forces in Earth pushing on rock formed a *syncline.*

taiga (tī′gə) A biome that contains many coniferous trees and in which rainfall is moderate. (D51) The *taiga* is south of the tundra.

taste bud A receptor on the surface of the tongue that responds to different substances and makes it possible to taste. (G38) There are only four basic types of *taste buds*.

tendon (ten′dən) A strong cord of tissue that joins a muscle to a bone. (G17) *Tendons* pull on bones like strings pull on the limbs of a puppet.

terrestrial planet (tə res′trē əl plan′it) An object in space that resembles Earth in size, in density, and in its mainly rocky composition. (B44) Mars is a *terrestrial planet*.

timbre (tam′bər) The quality of sound that sets one voice or musical instrument apart from another. (F58) The same note played on a violin and on a trumpet differ in *timbre*.

translucent (trans loo′sənt) Letting light through but scattering it; objects cannot be clearly seen through translucent material. (F48) The *translucent* glass dimmed the room.

transparent (trans per′ənt) Letting light through; objects can be clearly seen through transparent material. (F47) Window glass is usually *transparent* so that people can see through it.

transpiration (tran spə rā′shən) A process in which a plant releases moisture through its stomata. (A46) *Transpiration* adds water to the air.

tropical rain forest A biome distinguished by lush vegetation, abundant rainfall, and plentiful sunlight. (D50) The *tropical rain forest* supports the greatest variety of life of any biome.

tropism (trō′piz əm) A growth response of a plant to conditions in the environment, such as light or water. (A50) Growing toward a light source is an example of a plant *tropism*.

trough (trôf) The long narrow hollow between two waves. (F57) A *trough* occurs between two wave crests.

tundra (tun′drə) A biome characterized by cold temperatures and low precipitation. (D51) The *tundra* blooms in summer.

universe (yoo′nə vʉrs) The sum of everything that exists. (B70) Our solar system is part of the *universe*.

vacuole (vak′yoo ōl) A cell part that stores water and nutrients. (A24) Some plant cells have large *vacuoles*.

vacuum (vak′yoo əm) A space that is empty of any matter. (F17) Light waves can travel through a *vacuum*.

vibration A back-and-forth movement of matter. (F56) It is the *vibration* of the guitar strings that produces sound.

visible light A form of electromagnetic energy that can be seen. (F8) The eye responds to *visible light*.

volume The loudness or softness of a sound. (F78) Please turn up the *volume* on the radio.

water cycle A continuous process in which water moves between the atmosphere and Earth's surface, including its use by living things. (B87, D36) The *water cycle* is powered by energy from the Sun.

wave A disturbance that carries energy and that travels away from its starting point. (F17) The experiment measured how quickly light *waves* travel.

wavelength The distance between one crest of a wave and the next crest. (F17, F57) Red light has a longer *wavelength* than does blue light.

weathering The breaking up of rocks into sediments by such forces as wind, rain, and sunlight. (E62) Through *weathering*, igneous rock can be broken down into sediments.

wetland Any one of three ecosystems—marsh, swamp, or bog—where land and fresh water meet. (D53) *Wetlands* help purify water.

wheel and axle A simple machine made of two wheels of different sizes that pivot around the same point. (C58) A doorknob, along with its shaft, is an example of a *wheel and axle*.

white dwarf A very small, dying star that gives off very little light. (B65) When the Sun's fuel runs out, it will collapse into a *white dwarf*.

work The movement of a force through a distance. (C28) *Work* is done in lifting an object.

xylem cell (zī′ləm sel) A plant cell that, when joined with other similar cells, forms a transport system throughout a plant. (A11) The wood of a tree is formed mainly of *xylem cells*.

INDEX

Abiotic factors, D10, D48, D49
Absolute age, E79
Absorption (of colors/light), F47–F50
Acid, E45
Acupuncture, G46
Adaptations (plants), A48–A49*, A50–A52, A70–A72, A84–A85*, A86–A92
Addiction, G51, G53
Adobe, E55
Age
  absolute, E79
  relative, E78
AIDS, G53
Air, D16, F24, F26, F39
Alcohol, G50, G51, G56–G57*, G58–G60, G61–G62
  ads for, G56–G57*
  and driving, G61, G63
  damage to body, G59, G60
  fetal alcohol syndrome, G60
  in blood, G61–G62
  in pregnancy, G60
Alcoholics Anonymous (AA), G60
Alcoholism, G60
Algae, D16, D22
American Sign Language, F84
Ammonia, D41–D42
Amplitude, F57–F58, F70, F78
Animals, D4, D7*, D10, D13, D19, D21–D22, E45, E58
Anticline, E84–E85
Apatite, E15
Appalachian Mountains, E84–E85
Archaeoastronomy, B52
Astronomers, F28, F39

Audiocassettes, F92
Auditory nerve, F85, G39

Bacteria, D13, D19, E58
Basalt, E42, E57*
Battery, F7*
Bauxite, E12
Bedding (of rocks), E45
Benchmarks and Standards
  See *Project 2061 Benchmarks* and *National Science Education Standards*
Betelgeuse, B55*
Biceps, G14–G15*
Big–bang theory, B38–B39
Big Dipper, B11
Binary star, B67
Biodiversity, D58–D60, D61–D62
Biome, D46–D47*, D48–D51
Biosphere, B87
Biotic factors, D10
Birds, D10, D22
Black dwarf, B66
Black hole, B67, F40
Black light, F9. See also Ultraviolet radiation.
Blood, G10
  cells, G10
  vessels, G10
Blood alcohol concentration (BAC), G61–G62
Body, G4, G22
Bone(s), G4, G6*, G7*, G8–G9, G10–G11, G15*, G17–G18
  compact/spongy, G10
  injuries to, G19–G20
  marrow, G10
  periosteum, G10
Brain, G30–G33
  injury, G33

parts of, G31–G32
protective covering of, G30, G45
waves, G43–G44
Brain-actuated technology, G44
Breathing, D33*, D34. See also Respiration.
Bricks, E54–E55

Caffeine, G50
Calcite, E15–E16, E44, E45
Calorie, C19
Camera, F33–F34
Cancer, G51
Carbon, D35, E58
  compounds of, D35
Carbon dioxide, A33, A44–A45, A46, D16–D17, D33*, D34–D35, F9
Careers
  Acoustical Architect, F52
  Acupuncturist, G46
  Aerospace Project Engineer, B74
  Agricultural Researcher, A28
  Anthropologist, B52
  Astronomer, B4, F28
  Audiologist, F74
  Avionics and Radar Technician, B28
  Biologist, D44
  Botanist, A4
  Ecologist, D4
  Environmental Engineer, D24
  Dredge Operator-Supervisor, E4
  Mechanical Engineer, C4
  Neurobiologist, G24
  Physical Therapist, G4
  Plant Wildlife Specialist, A54
  Professional Tennis Player, C36

*Activity
Blue entries indicate Teaching Guide material.

*Activity
Blue entries indicate Teaching Guide material.

F47
concave, F30*, F32,
F34–F35
convex, F30*, F31, F32–F35
eyepiece, F41
magnifying, F32.
objective, F41
Lever, C46–C47*, C48–C49*,
C50–C52, C53–C55
fulcrum, C46*, C50, C53
pulley, C48–C49*, C53–C55,
C62
Lichens, D22
Ligaments, G8, G12, G20
Light, F4, F6*, F8, F10, F12,
F16, F17, F20*, F22,
F30–F31*, F32–F33, F35,
F38–F39, F41, F43,
F44–F45*, F46, F48
bending of, F32–F33
filtering of, F44*, F46*,
F48–F50
rays, F23, F24–F25, F32,
F34, F41
source, F6*, F10
speed of, F17, F24, F25
visible, F8–F9, F19, F47
waves, F14, F17, F24, F25
white, F47, F49
Light bulb, F7*, F10–F11
Light-year, B61
Lightning, D12, F11
Lignite, E58
Limestone, E44, E45, E52,
E57*
Little Dipper, B11
Liver, G59, G60
Living things, D6–D7*, D10
Luster, E7, E13–E14, E17
of minerals, E7, E13–E14,
E18

Machines, C38–C62,
C38–C39*, C40*, C41*,
C46–C47*, C48–C49*,
C56–C57*
compound, C61–C62
gear, C60
inclined plane, C40*, C41*,
C42, C43–C45, C61
lever, C46–C47*, C48–C49*,

C50–C52, C53–C55
pulley, C48–C49*, C53–C55,
C62
ramp, C38–C39*, C40*,
C41*, C42, C43–C45
wheel and axle, C56–C57*,
C58–C59, C60
Magellan spacecraft, B28
Magma, E40–E41, E47, E60
Magnetic Resonance Imaging
(MRI), G20
Magnetite, E27–E28
Magnifying, F32, F38,
F41–F42
Mammals, D13, D18, D19
Mantle, E69
Marble, E49, E52, E57*
Marrow, G10
Mars, B45
Mating, D11
Matter, D32*, F8, F10
Mechanical advantage, C45
Medicines, A21, A63, D62,
G50, G63
over-the-counter, G50
prescription, G50
Medulla, G32
Memory, G34–G35*
Mercury, B44
Metamorphic rocks, E47,
E48–E49, E50*, E55,
E58–E62, E79, E90
Metamorphism, E47–E48
Meteorite, B20*, B26
Meteors, B25–B26
Mica, E15, E41, E48
Micmacs, B15
Microscope, F41–F42
electron, F43
simple/compound, F41–F42
Microscopic organisms, D16,
D21
Microsurgery, F16
Microwaves, F19
Milky Way Galaxy, B70–B72
Mineral(s), E4, E6–E7*,
E12–E16, E34, E36–E37*,
E43, E44, E48, E54, E60
and crystals, E22–E23,
E36–E37*
cleavage planes, E10–E11*
grains in, E40–E42, E48–E49
hardness of, E13–E14, E17

identifying, E17–E19
metal resources in, E30–E32
production of, E31
properties of, E8–E9*,
E12–E16
recycling of, E31–E32
streak test, E7
Mirrors, F20*, F22, F39, F40,
F41
concave, F23, F39
convex/plane, F23
Misconceptions
A4, A28, A54, A74, B4,
B28, B52, B74, C4, C36,
D4, D24, D44, E4, E36,
E64, F4, F28, F52, F74, G4,
G24, G46
Model, E68
Mohs scale of hardness, E13
Molten rock, E40–E42, E47,
E60
Monocot, A81
Moon(s), B44, F28, F38, F40
Morning star, B16
Mosses, A78
Motor neurons, G28–G29, G42
Mount St. Helens, D12–D13
Mountains, E80–E81*, E82*,
E83*, E84–E87, E88–E89*,
E92
Multi-age Classroom
A24, A38, A42, A44, A45,
A50, A60, A71, B13, B34,
B35, B38, B45, B48, B63,
C21, C33, D12, D19, E9,
E41, E44, E45, E69, E70,
E76, E78, E83, F16, F33,
F47, F69, F85, F90, F91,
G8, G10, G18, G28, G29,
G30, G31, G42, G50, G54,
G59
Multi-age Strategies
A40, A64, A84, B18, B42,
B68, B82, B84, B88, C6,
C16, C24, C40, D6, D28,
D46, D51, D54, D60, E11,
E50, F89, G14, G26, G27,
G34, G56
Muscles, G4, G14–G15*, G16*,
G17–G19
biceps, G14–G15*, G18
cardiac, G17
cramping of, G20

*Activity
Blue entries indicate Teaching Guide material.

Pressure (on rocks), E48,
E58–E60
Prey, D21
Prism, F47
Producers, A36–A39, D18,
D26–D27*, D28*, D29–D30
Project 2061 Benchmarks
A1c, B1c, C1c, D1c, E1c,
F1c, G1c
Proteins, D41
Protostars, B65
Proxima Centauri, B61
Ptolemy, B36–B37
Pulley, C48–C49*, C53–C55,
C62
Pyrite, E15–E16
Pyroxine, E41

Quarry, E52–E53
Quartz, E13, E24, E41, E48
elements of, E24–E26
used in computers, E25–E26
used in concrete, E24
used in glass, E25
Quartzite, E56*
Quinine, A21

Radiation, C11
Radio telescope, B92–B94
Radio waves, F19, F25
Rain, D10–D11
Rainbow, F47
Rain forest, A20, A27, A38,
A92, D11, D37, D50,
D56–D57*, D60
and deforestation, A92
Ramp, C38–C39*, C40*, C41*,
C42, C43–C45
Rarefaction, F56–F57
Reaction, G27*, G28
Receptors, G37
Red giant, B65
Reflection, F22, F25, F39,
F41, F47, F49
Reflex, G36*, G42, G45
Reforestation in Kenya, D44
Refraction, F24–F26, F32,
F38, F47

Relative age, E78
Reproduction (plants), A58*,
A59–A63, A64–A65*,
A66–A67, A73
asexual, A62–A63
sexual, A59–A61
Resistance force, C30,
C50–C52, C53–C55,
C58–C59
Respiration, A35, A40–A41*,
A44–A45, D34–D35
Revolution, B13–B14
Ribs, G11
Rock(s), D10, E34, E36–E37*,
E38–E39*, E43, E46, E47,
E50–E51*, E52–E56,
E74–E75*, E77–E79, E90
absolute age of, E79
classification of, E40
crystalline, E50*
grain of, E38–E39*
hardness of, E38–E39*
igneous, E40–E41, E47,
E50*, E60–E62, E79, E90
metamorphic, E47, E50*,
E55, E58–E59, E60–E62,
E79, E90
order layers formed,
E74–E75*
particles in, E51*
relative age of, E78
sedimentary, E43, E45–E47,
E50*, E58–E59, E60–E62,
E77
texture of, E47
Rock cycle, E56–E57*, E60
Rock key, E38*, E46
Rock quarry, E52–E53
Rock salt, E44
Roots, A8–A9*, A10–A11
transport, A11, A13
Rotation, B13–B14

Sand, E55, E56–E57*
Sandstone, E34, E43–E44,
E52, E56–E57*
Sapling, A67
Satellite, B44
Saturn, B48
Science in Literature
A20, A38, A71, A80, B25,

B46, B66, B93, C30, C52,
D21, D39, D57, E14, E45,
E84, F25, F42, F58, F80,
G21, G32, G60
Science Process Skills
Classifying, A1g, B1g, C1g,
D1g, E1g, F1g, G1g
Collecting, Recording, and
Interpreting Data, A1g, B1g,
C1g, D1g, E1g, F1g, G1g
Communicating, A1g, B1g,
C1g, D1g, E1g, F1g, G1g
Defining Operationally, A1g,
B1g, C1g, D1g, E1g, F1g,
G1g
Experimenting, A1g, B1g,
C1g, D1g, E1g, F1g, G1g
Identifying and Controlling
Variables, A1g, B1g, C1g,
D1g, E1g, F1g, G1g
Inferring, A1g, B1g, C1g,
D1g, E1g, F1g, G1g
Making and Using Models,
A1g, B1g, C1g, D1g, E1g,
F1g, G1g
Making Hypotheses, A1g,
B1g, C1g, D1g, E1g, F1g,
G1g
Measuring/Using Numbers,
A1g, B1g, C1g, D1g, E1g,
F1g, G1g
Observing, A1g, B1g, C1g,
D1g, E1g, F1g, G1g
Predicting, A1g, B1g, C1g,
D1g, E1g, F1g, G1g
**Science, Technology &
Society**
A20, A34, A38, A60, A80,
A88, B22, B44, B64, B93,
C19, C53, C59, C60, D10,
D29, D51, E12, E18, E25,
E58, E70, E91, F11, F23,
F41, F71, F79, F90, G21,
G43, G54
Scientific Reasoning Skills
Consideration of Conse-
quences, A1h, B1h, C1h,
D1h, E1h, F1h, G1h
Consideration of Premises,
A1h, B1h, C1h, D1h, E1h,
F1h, G1h
Demand for Verification, A1h,
B1h, C1h, D1h, E1h, F1h,

*Activity
Blue entries indicate Teaching Guide material.

*Activity
Blue entries indicate Teaching Guide material.